The TI-83/TI-83 Plus Manual

Kathleen McLaughlin
Dorothy Wakefield

SECOND EDITION

ELEMENTARY STATISTICS

Picturing the World

LARSON • FARBER

Prentice Hall

Upper Saddle River, NJ 07458

Editor in Chief: Sally Yagan
Acquisitions Editor: Quincy McDonald
Supplement Editor: Joanne Wendelken
Assistant Managing Editor: John Matthews
Production Editor: Donna Crilly
Supplement Cover Designer: Paul Gourhan
Manufacturing Buyer: Ilene Kahn

© 2003 by Pearson Education
Pearson Education, Inc.
Upper Saddle River, NJ 07458

Printed in the United States of America

10 9 8 7 6 5 4 3

ISBN 0-13-065949-5

Pearson Education Ltd., *London*
Pearson Education Australia Pty. Ltd., *Sydney*
Pearson Education Singapore, Pte. Ltd.
Pearson Education North Asia Ltd., *Hong Kong*
Pearson Education Canada, Inc., *Toronto*
Pearson Educacíon de Mexico, S.A. de C.V.
Pearson Education—Japan, *Tokyo*
Pearson Education Malaysia, Pte. Ltd.
Pearson Education, *Upper Saddle River, New Jersey*

▶ Introduction

The TI-83 and TI-83 Plus Graphing Calculator Manual is one of a series of companion technology manuals that provide hands-on technology assistance to users of Larson/Farber *Elementary Statistics: Picturing the World.*

Detailed instructions for working selected examples, exercises, and Technology Labs from *Elementary Statistics: Picturing the World* are provided in this manual. To make the correlation with the text as seamless as possible, the table of contents includes page references for both the Larson/Farber text and this manual.

▶ Contents:

Getting Started with the TI-83 and TI-83 Plus Graphing Calculators

▸ Overview

This manual is designed to be used with the TI-83 or TI-83 Plus graphing calculator. These calculators have a variety of useful functions for doing statistical calculations and for creating statistical plots. The commands for using the statistical functions are the same for both calculators. The main difference between the two calculators is that the TI-83 Plus has the capability of downloading a variety of software applications that are available through the TI website (www.ti.com). TI also will provide downloadable updates to the TI-83 Plus operating system. These features are not available on the TI-83. Throughout this manual all references to the TI-83 are actually references to both the TI-83 and TI-83 Plus.

Before you begin using the TI-83, spend a few minutes becoming familiar with its basic operations. First, notice the different colored keys on the calculator. The gray keys are the number keys. The blue keys along the right side of the keyboard are the common math functions. The blue keys across the top set up and display graphs. The primary function of each key is printed in white on the key. For example, when you press STAT, the STAT MENU is displayed.

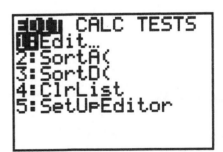

The secondary function of each key is printed in yellow above the key. When you press the 2nd key, the function printed in yellow above the key becomes active and the cursor changes from a solid rectangle to an ↑ (up-arrow). For example, when you press 2nd and the $\boxed{x^2}$ key, the $\sqrt{}$ function is activated. In this manual, all 2nd functions are highlighted in gray. For example, to use the

LIST function, found above the STAT key, the notation used in this manual is 2nd [LIST]. The LIST MENU will then be activated and displayed on the screen.

The alpha function of each key is printed in green above the key. When you press the green ALPHA key, the function printed in green above the key is activated and the cursor changes from a solid rectangle to A.

In this manual you will find detailed explanations of the different statistical functions. These explanations will accompany selected examples from your textbook.

▶ Getting Started

To operate the calculator, press ON in the lower left corner of the calculator. Begin each example with a blank screen, with a rectangular cursor flashing in the upper left corner. If you turn on your calculator and you do not have a blank screen, press the CLEAR key. You may have to press CLEAR a second time in order to clear the screen. If using the CLEAR key does not clear the screen, you can push 2nd [QUIT] (Note: QUIT is found above the MODE key.)

▶ Helpful Hints

To adjust the display contrast, push and release the 2nd key. Then push and hold the blue up arrow ▲ to darken or the blue down arrow ▼ to lighten.

The calculator has an automatic turn off that will turn the calculator off if it has been idle for several minutes. To restart, simply press the ON key.

There are several different graphing techniques available on the TI-83. If you inadvertently leave a graph on and attempt to use a different graphing function, your graph display may be cluttered with extraneous graphs, or you may get an ERROR message on the screen.

There are several items that you should check before graphing anything. First, press the ▓ key and clear all the Y-variables. The screen should look like the following display:

If there are any functions stored in the Y-variables, simply move the cursor to the line that isn't clear and press CLEAR ENTER.

Next, press 2nd [STAT PLOT] and check to make sure that all the STAT PLOTS are turned **OFF**.

If you notice that a Plot is turned **ON**, select the Plot, press ENTER and move the cursor to **OFF** and press ENTER. Press 2nd [QUIT] to return to the home screen.

Introduction to Statistics

CHAPTER

1

▶ Technology Lab (pg. 22-23) Generating Random Numbers

To generate a random sample of integers, press **MATH** and the Math Menu will appear.

```
MATH NUM CPX PRB
1:▶Frac
2:▶Dec
3:³
4:³√(
5:ˣ√
6:fMin(
7↓fMax(
```

Use the blue right arrow key, **▶**, to move the cursor to highlight **PRB**. The Probability Menu will appear.

```
MATH NUM CPX PRB
1:rand
2:nPr
3:nCr
4:!
5:randInt(
6:randNorm(
7:randBin(
```

Select **5:RandInt(** by using the blue down arrow key, **▼** , to highlight it and pressing **ENTER** or by pressing the **5** key. **RandInt(** should appear on the screen. This function requires three values: the starting integer, followed by a comma (the comma is found on the black key above the **7** key), the ending integer, followed by a comma and the number of values you want to generate. Close the parentheses and press **ENTER**. (Note: It is optional to close the parenthesis at the end of the command.)

For an example, suppose you want to generate 15 values from the integers ranging from 1 to 50. The command is **randInt(1,50,15)**.

Press **ENTER** and a partial display of the 15 random integers should appear on your screen. (Note: your numbers will be different from the ones you see here.)

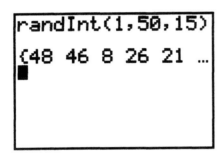

Use the right arrow to scroll through your 15 items. You might find that you have some duplicate values. The TI-83 uses a method called "sampling with replacement" to generate random numbers. This means that it is possible to select the same integer twice.

In the example in the text, you are asked to select a random sample of 15 cars from the 167 cars that are assembled at an auto plant. One way to choose the sample is to number the cars from 1 to 167 and randomly select 15 different cars. This sampling process is to be "without replacement." Since the TI-83 samples "with replacement", the best way to obtain 15 different cars is to generate more than 15 random integers, and to discard any duplicates. To be safe, you should generate 20 random integers.

Use the right arrow to scroll to the right to see the rest of the list and write down the first 15 distinct values.

Exercises

1. You would like to sample 8 distinct accounts. The TI-83 samples "with replacement" so you may have duplicates in your sample. To obtain 8 distinct values, try selecting 10 items. Press **MATH**, highlight **PRB** and select **5:RandInt(**. Press **ENTER** and type in **1,74,10).** Press **ENTER** and the random integers will appear on the screen. Use the right arrow to scroll through the output and choose the first eight distinct integers. (Note: If you don't have 8 distinct integers, generate 10 more integers and pick as many new integers as you need from this group to complete your sample of 8).

2. Because you want 20 distinct batteries, generate 25 random integers using **randInt(1,200,25).** Use the right arrow to scroll through the list and select the first 20 distinct integers.

3. This example does not require distinct digits, so duplicates are allowed. You can select three random samples of size n=5 by using **randInt** to create each sample. To generate the first sample, press **MATH**, highlight **PRB** and select **5:RandInt(** by scrolling down through the list and highlighting **5:RandInt(** and pressing **ENTER** or by highlighting **PRB** and pressing **5**. Type in the starting digit: 0; the ending digit: 9, and the number of selections: 5.

Add the digits and divide by 5 to get the average for the sample.

To generate the second and third samples, repeat this process two more times. Calculate the sample average for the 2nd and 3rd sample.

To calculate the population average, add the digits 0 through 9 and divide the answer by 10.

Compare your three sample averages with your population average.

4. Use the same procedure as in Exercise 3 with a starting value of 0 and an ending value of 40 and a sample size of 7.

5. Use **randInt(1,6,60).** Store the results in L1 by pressing STO 2nd [L1] ENTER. (Note: [L1] is found above the 1 key.) Then sort L1 by pressing 2nd [LIST], ([LIST is found above the STAT key), highlight **OPS** and select **1:SortA(** and press 2nd [L1] ENTER. Press 2nd [L1] ENTER and a partial list of the integers in L1 will appear on the screen. Use the right arrow to scroll through the list and count the number of 1's, 2's, 3's, ... and 6's. Record the results in a table.

7.   Use **randInt(0,1,100).** Store the results in L1. Press $\boxed{2^{nd}}$ **[LIST]** , highlight
     MATH and select **5:sum(** and press $\boxed{2^{nd}}$ **[L1].** Close the parentheses and
     press ENTER.

The number in your output is the sum of L1. Since L1 consists of 0's and 1's,
the sum is actually the number of tails in your random sample. The (number
of heads) = 100 - (no. of tails).

Descriptive Statistics

Section 2.1

▶ **Example 7 (pg. 40)** Construct a histogram using Internet data

To create this histogram, you must enter information into List1 **(L1)** and List 2 **(L2)**. Refer to the frequency distribution on pg. 35 in your textbook. You will enter the midpoints into **L1** and the frequencies into **L2**. Press **STAT** and the Statistics Menu will appear.

Press **ENTER** and lists **L1, L2** and **L3** will appear.

If the lists already contain data, you should clear them before beginning this example. Move your cursor so that the List name **(L1, L2,** or **L3)** of the list that contains data is highlighted.

```
 ▓1      L2      L3      1

  1        4       ------
  2        6
  3        8
 10
------

L1 ={1,2,3,10}
```

Press **CLEAR** **ENTER**. Repeat this process until all three lists are empty.

```
L1       L2      L3      1

▓▓▓▓▓▓    4       ------
          6
          8
          ------

L1(1)=
```

To enter the midpoints into **L1,** move your cursor so that it is positioned in the 1st position in **L1**. Type in the first midpoint, **12.5,** and press **ENTER** or use the blue down arrow. Enter the next midpoint, **24.5**. Continue this process until all 7 midpoints are entered into **L1**. Now use the blue up-arrow to scroll to the top of **L1**. As you scroll through the data, check it. If a data point is incorrect, simply move the cursor to highlight it and type in the correct value. When you have moved to the 1st value in **L1**, use the right arrow to move to the first position in **L2**. Enter the frequencies into **L2**.

```
L1       L2      L3      2

12.5     6       ------
24.5     10
36.5     13
48.5     8
60.5     5
72.5     6
84.5     2

L2(1)=6
```

To graph the histogram, press **2nd** [STAT PLOT] (located above the **Y=** key).

Select Plot1 by pressing **ENTER**.

Notice that Plot1 is highlighted. On the next line, notice that the cursor is flashing on **ON** or **OFF**. Position the cursor on **ON** and press **ENTER** to select it. The next two lines on the screen show the different types of graphs. Move your cursor to the symbol for histogram (3rd item in the 1st line of **Type)** and press **ENTER**.

The next line is **Xlist**. Use the blue down arrow to move to this line. On this line, you tell the calculator where the data (the midpoints) are stored. In most graphing situations, the data are entered into **L1** so **L1** is the default option. Notice that the cursor is flashing on **L1**. Push **ENTER** to select **L1**. The last line is the frequency line. On this line, **1** is the default. The cursor should be flashing on **1**. Change 1 to **L2** by pressing **2nd [L2]**.

To view a histogram of the data, press **ZOOM**.

There are several options in the Zoom Menu. Using the blue down arrow, scroll down to option 9, **ZoomStat,** and press **ENTER**. A histogram should appear on the screen.

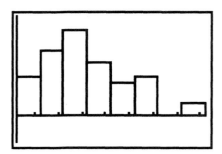

This histogram is not exactly the same as the one on pg. 40 of your textbook. You can adjust the histogram so that it does look exactly like the one in your text. Press **Window** and set **Xmin** to 12.5, **Xmax** to 96.5 (this one extra midpoint is needed to complete the picture), and **Xscl** equal to 12, which is the difference between successive midpoints in the frequency distribution. Note: It is not necessary for you to make any changes to **Ymin**, **Ymax** or **Yscl**.

```
WINDOW
 Xmin=12.5
 Xmax=96.5
 Xscl=12
 Ymin=-3.90897
 Ymax=15.21
 Yscl=.1
 Xres=1
```

Press **GRAPH**.

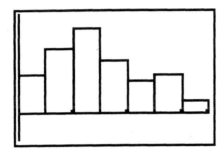

Notice the blue **TRACE** key. If you press it, a flashing cursor, ✳, will appear at the top of the 1ˢᵗ bar of the histogram.

The value of the smallest midpoint is displayed as 12.5 and the number of data points in that bar is displayed as n = 6. Use the blue right arrow to move through each of the bars.

Now that you have completed this example, turn Plot1 **OFF**. Using **2ⁿᵈ** [STAT PLOT], select Plot1 by pressing **ENTER** and highlighting **OFF**. Press **ENTER** and **2ⁿᵈ** [QUIT]. (Note: Turning Plot1 **OFF** is optional. You can leave it ON but leaving it ON will effect other graphing operations of the calculator.)

◀

▶ Exercise 17 (pg. 43) Construct a frequency histogram using 6
classes

Push **STAT** and **ENTER** to select **1:Edit**. Highlight **L1** at the top of the first list
and press **CLEAR** and **ENTER** to clear the data in **L1**. You can also clear **L2**
although you will not be using **L2** in this example. Enter the data into **L1**. Scroll
through your completed list and verify each entry.

To set up the histogram, push **2ⁿᵈ [STAT PLOT]** and **ENTER** to select **Plot 1**.
Turn ON **Plot 1**, set **Type** to **Histogram**, set **Xlist** to **L1**. In this example, you
must set **Freq** to 1. If the frequency is set on **L2** move the cursor so that it is
flashing on **L2** and press **CLEAR**. The cursor is now in ALPHA mode (notice
that there is an "A" flashing in the cursor). Push the **ALPHA** key and the cursor
should return to a solid flashing square. Type in the number **1.**

```
Plot1  Plot2  Plot3
On Off
Type: ⌐∙  ⌐∠  ⫿⫿⫿
      ⊞⊡  ⊞⊡  ∠
Xlist:L₁
Freq:1
```

Press **ZOOM** and **9:ZoomStat** and press **ENTER** and a histogram will appear on
the screen. Press **Window** to adjust the Graph Window. Set **Xmin** equal to 1000
(the smallest data value) and **Xmax** equal to 7200 (a value, rounded to the
nearest hundred, that is larger than the largest data point in the dataset). To set
the scale so that you will have 6 classes, calculate (**Xmax - Xmin**)/6. Round this
number to the next highest tens (1020) and use this for **Xscl**. (Note: You do not
need to change the values for **Ymin**, **Ymax** or **Yscl**.)

```
WINDOW
 Xmin=1000
 Xmax=7120
 Xscl=1020
 Ymin=-3.90897
 Ymax=15.21
 Yscl=.1
 Xres=1
```

Press GRAPH and the histogram should appear.

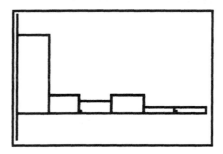

You can press TRACE and scroll through the bars of the histogram.
Min and Max values for each bar will appear along with the number of data
points in each class.

Notice, for example, with the cursor highlighting the second bar of the histogram,
you will see that **n=3** appears, indicating that there are 3 data points in the second
class (2020-3039)

Section 2.2

▶ **Example 5 (pg. 50)** Constructing a Pareto Chart

To construct a Pareto chart to represent the causes of inventory shrinkage, you must enter the causes of inventory shrinkage. Enter labels for the specific causes into **L1** and the costs into **L2**. Since the bars are positioned in descending order in a Pareto chart, the labels in **L1** will represent the causes of inventory shrinkage from the most costly to the least costly. Press **STAT** and select **1:Edit** and press **ENTER**. Highlight the name "**L1**" and press **CLEAR** and **ENTER**. Enter the numbers 1,2,3 and 4 into **L1**. These numbers represent the four causes of inventory shrinkage: 1 = employee theft, 2 = shoplifting, 3 = administrative error and 4 = vendor fraud. Move your cursor to highlight "**L2**" and press **CLEAR** and **ENTER**. Enter the values 15.6, 14.7, 7.8 and 2.9.

```
L1      L2      L3      2
1       15.6    ------
2       14.7
3       7.8
4       2.9
------

L2(5) =
```

To draw the Pareto chart, press **2ⁿᵈ [STAT PLOT]** . Press **ENTER** and set up **Plot 1**. Highlight **On** and press **ENTER**. Highlight the histogram icon for **Type** and press **ENTER**. Set **Xlist** to **L1** and **Freq** to **L2**.

Press **ZOOM** and select **9:ZoomStat** and **ENTER**.

To adjust the picture so that the bars are connected press **Window**. Set **Xmax** = 5 . (Note: The numbers in **L1** range from 1 to 4. To create the bars in the Pareto, **Xmax** should be set at 5, which is one value greater than the largest value in **L1**.) Set **Xscl** = 1, and press **GRAPH**.. (Note: You do not need to change the values for **Ymin, Ymax** or **Yscl**.)

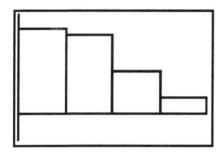

If you press **TRACE**, notice min=1, max < 2 and n = 15.6. min =1 is the minimum value of the 1st bar. In this example, the first bar represents the No. 1 cause of inventory shrinkage. N = 15.6 is the frequency (in millions of dollars) for cause #1. You can use the right arrow key to scroll through the remaining causes.

◀

▶ Example 7 (pg. 52) Constructing a Time Series Chart

Press **STAT** and select **1:Edit** from the **Edit Menu**. Clear **L1** and **L2**. Enter the "years" into **L1** and the "subscribers" into **L2**.

L1	L2	L3 2
1987	1.2	------
1988	2.1	
1989	3.5	
1990	5.3	
1991	7.6	
1992	11	
1993	16	

L2 ={1.2,2.1,3.5...

To construct the time series chart, press **2ⁿᵈ [STAT PLOT]** and select **1:Plot 1** and **ENTER**. Turn ON **Plot 1**. Set the **Type** to **Scatterplot,** which is the 1ˢᵗ icon in the **Type** choices. For **Xlist** select **L1** and for **Ylist** select **L2**. Next, there are three different types of **Marks** that you can select for the graph. The first choice, a small square, is the best one to use.

Press **ZOOM** and scroll down to **9:ZoomStat** and press **ENTER** or simply press **9** and **ZoomStat** will automatically be selected. The graph should appear on the screen.

Use **TRACE** to scroll through the data values for each year. Notice for example, the number of subscribers is 24.1 million in 1994.

▶ Exercise 23 (pg. 55) Pareto Chart

Press **STAT** and select **1:Edit** from the **Edit Menu**. Clear the lists and enter the numbers 1 through 5 into **L1**. These numbers are labels for the five cities. (Note: 1= Miami, the city with the highest ultraviolet index, 2 = Atlanta, the city with the second highest ultraviolet index, etc.). Enter the ultraviolet indices in descending order into **L2**. Press **2ⁿᵈ** [STAT PLOT] and select **Plot 1** and press **ENTER**. Set the **Type** to **Histogram**. Set **Xlist** to **L1** and Freq to **L2**. Press **ZOOM** and press **9** for **ZoomStat.** Adjust the graph by pressing **Window** and setting **Xmax** = 6 (one value higher than the largest value in **L1**) and **Xscl** = 1. (Note: You do not need to change the values for **Ymin**, **Ymax** or **Yscl**.) Press **GRAPH** to view the Pareto Chart.

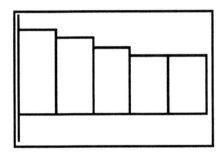

▶ Exercise 25 (pg. 56) Scatterplot

Press **STAT** and select **1:Edit** from the **Edit menu**. Clear the lists and enter the data points for"number of students per teacher" into **L1** and the data points for"average Teacher's salary" into **L2**.
To construct the scatterplot, press **2ⁿᵈ** [STAT PLOT] and select **1:Plot 1** and **ENTER**. Turn ON **Plot 1**. Set the **Type** to **Scatterplot** which is the 1ˢᵗ icon in the **Type** choices. For **Xlist** select **L1** and for **Ylist** select **L2**. For **Marks** use the first choice, the small square.

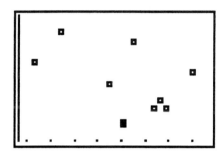

As you can see from the scatterplot, this data set has a large amount of scatter. You might notice a slight downward trend that suggests that the average teacher's salary decreases as the number of students per teacher increases.

◀

> ▶ **Exercise 27 (pg. 56)** Time Series Chart

Press **STAT** and select **1:Edit**. Enter the "Years" into **L1** and the "prices" into **L2**. Press **2ⁿᵈ** **[STAT PLOT]** and select 1: **Plot 1** and press **ENTER**. Turn **ON** **Plot 1** and select the **scatterplot** (1ˢᵗ icon) as **Type**. Set **Xlist** to **L1** and **Ylist** to **L2** and Mark to ■. Press **ZOOM** and press ⑨ for **ZoomStat** and view the graph.

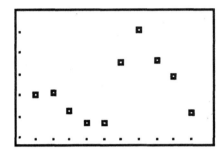

◀

Section 2.3

▶ Example 6 (pg. 60) Comparing the mean, median, and mode

Press **STAT** and select **1:Edit**. Clear **L1** and enter the data into **L1**. Press **STAT** again and highlight **CALC** to view the Calc Menu.

```
EDIT CALC TESTS
1:1-Var Stats
2:2-Var Stats
3:Med-Med
4:LinReg(ax+b)
5:QuadReg
6:CubicReg
7↓QuartReg
```

Select **1:1-Var Stats.** On this line, enter the name of the column that contains the data. Since you have stored the data in **L1,** simply enter **2ⁿᵈ [L1] ENTER** and the first page of the one variable statistics will appear. (Note: If you did not enter a column name, the default column, which is **L1,** would be automatically selected.)

```
1-Var Stats L1
```

```
1-Var Stats
 x̄=23.75
 Σx=475
 Σx²=13109
 Sx=9.808025715
 σx=9.559680957
↓n=20
```

The first item is the mean, $\bar{x} = 23.75$. Notice the down arrow in the bottom left corner of the screen. This indicates that more information follows this first page. Use the blue down arrow to scroll through this information. The third item you see on the second page is the median, Med = 21.5.

The TI-83 does not calculate the mode but, since this data set is sorted, it is easy to see from the list of data that the mode is 20.

▸ Example 7 (pg. 61) Finding a Weighted Mean

Press **STAT** and select **1:Edit**. Clear **L1** and **L2**. Enter the scores into **L1** and the weights into **L2**.

```
L1      L2      L3     2
86      .5      ------
96      .15
82      .2
98      .1
100     .05

L2(6) =
```

Press **STAT** and highlight **CALC** to view the Calc Menu. Select **1:1-Var Stats**, press **ENTER** and press 2nd **[L1]** ⎜ 2nd **[L2]** . Press **ENTER**. (Note: You must place the comma between **L1** and **L2**).

```
1-Var Stats L1,L
2
```

Using **L1** and **L2** in the **1:1-Var Stats** calculation is necessary when calculating a weighted mean. The calculator uses the data in **L1** and the associated weights in **L2** to calculate the average. In this example, the weighted mean is **88.6**.

```
1-Var Stats
 x̄=88.6
 Σx=88.6
 Σx²=7885.6
 Sx=
 σx=5.969924623
↓n=1
```

◀

> ▶ **Example 8 (pg. 62)** Finding the Mean of a Frequency
> Distribution

Press **STAT** and select **1:Edit**. Clear **L1** and **L2**. Enter the x-values into **L1** and the frequencies into **L2**. Press **STAT**, highlight **CALC**, select **1:1-Var Stats**, press **ENTER**. Next, press **2nd [L1]** ⎵ **2nd [L2] ENTER**.

After you press **ENTER**, the sample statistics will appear on the screen. The mean of the frequency distribution described in columns **L1** and **L2** is 41.78. In this example you do not have the actual data. What you have is the frequency distribution of the data summarized into categories. The mean of this frequency distribution is an approximation of the mean of the actual data.

```
1-Var Stats
 x̄=41.78
 Σx=2089
 Σx²=107196.5
 Sx=20.16163259
 σx=19.95899797
↓n=50
■
```

◀

▶ Exercise 19 (pg. 65) Finding the Mean, Median and Mode

Enter the data into **L1**. Press **STAT** and select **1:1-Var Stats** from the Calc Menu. Press **L1** **ENTER**.

```
1-Var Stats
 x̄=97
 Σx=2716
 Σx²=263903.82
 Sx=4.090730262
 σx=4.017017373
↓n=28
```

The first item in the output screen is the mean, 97. Scroll down through the output and find the median, Med = 97.2.

```
1-Var Stats
↑n=28
 minX=87.5
 Q₁=95.05
 Med=97.2
 Q₃=100.1
 maxX=103.1
■
```

Although the TI-83 does not calculate the mode, you can use the SORT feature to order the data. You can then scroll through the data to see if the data set contains a mode. To sort the data, press **2ⁿᵈ** **[LIST]** (Note: **List** is found above the **STAT** key). Move the cursor to highlight **OPS** and select **1:SortA(** and **ENTER**.

To sort **L1** in ascending order, press **2nd** **[L1]** , close the parentheses and press
ENTER.

To view the data, press STAT and select **1:Edit** and press ENTER. Use the down arrow to scroll through **L1** to see if the data has a mode. In this example, there is no mode because there is no individual data value that occurs more often than all the others. (Most of the data values occur only once and there are four data values that occur twice.)

L1	L2	L3	2
87.5		------	
89.2			
90.5			
90.6			
94.2			
94.8			
94.8			
L2(1)=			

▶ Exercise 37 (pg. 67) Finding the Mean of Grouped Data

Press **STAT** and select **1:Edit**. Clear **L1** and **L2**. Enter the midpoints of each Age group into **L1** and the frequencies into **L2**.

L1	**L2**	L3	2
4.5	57	------	
14.5	68		
24.5	36		
34.5	55		
44.5	71		
54.5	44		
64.5	36		

L2 = {57, 68, 36, 55...

Press **STAT** and highlight **CALC** to view the Calc Menu. Select **1:1-Var Stats**, press **ENTER** and type in **L1** , **L2.** The mean of this grouped data is 35.01.

```
1-Var Stats
 x̄=35.01413882
 Σx=13620.5
 Σx²=658407.25
 Sx=21.62813485
 σx=21.6003173
↓n=389
```

◀

▶ **Exercise 41 (pg. 68)** Construct a frequency histogram

Press **STAT** and select **1:Edit**. Clear **L1** and enter the data into **L1**. Press **2nd** [STAT PLOT] and select **1:Plot 1** and press **ENTER**. Turn **ON** Plot 1 and set the **Type** to **Histogram** and press **ENTER**. Move the cursor to **Xlist** and set this to **L1**. Move the cursor to **Freq** and set it equal to **1.** (Note: The cursor may be in **ALPHA** mode with a flashing $\boxed{A}$. Press **ALPHA** to return to the solid rectangular cursor and type in **1** .

Press **ZOOM** and **9** to select **ZoomStat**. The histogram that is displayed has 7 classes. To change to 5 classes, press **Window**. Notice that **Xmin** = 62 and **Xmax** = 78.33. To determine a value for **Xscl**, you must calculate (**Xmax - Xmin**)/5. Press **2nd** **[QUIT]** to get out of the Window Menu. (Note: QUIT is found above the **MODE** key). Calculate (78.33 - 62)/5 and round the resulting value, 3.3, to 3. Press **Window** and set **Xscl** = 3. Set **Xmax** = 79, which is the next whole number greater than 78.333. Press **GRAPH** and view the histogram with 5 classes. Notice that one of the bars is too tall to fit completely on the screen. Press **Window** and set **Ymax** = 9, which is the next whole number greater than 8.19. Press **GRAPH** again. As you can see from the graph, the histogram appears to be symmetric.

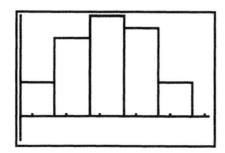

Exercise 47 (pg. 69) Data Analysis

Press STAT and select **1:Edit**. Clear **L1** and then enter the data. Press STAT and highlight **CALC**. Select **1:1-Var Stats** and press L1 ENTER to get values for the mean and median.

Since the TI-83 does not do a stem and leaf display, you can use a histogram to get a picture of the data. Press 2nd [STAT PLOT] , select **1:Plot 1** and press ENTER. Turn **ON Plot 1**. Set **Type** to **Histogram**. The **Xlist** is **L1** and the **Freq** is **1**. Press ZOOM and 9 to select **ZoomStat.**

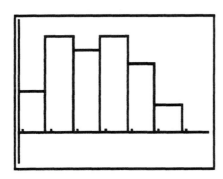

◀

Section 2.4

▶ **Example 5 (pg. 74)** Finding the Standard Deviation

Press **STAT** and select **1:Edit**. Clear **L1** and enter the data into **L1**. Press
STAT and highlight **CALC** to display the Calc Menu. Select **1: 1-Var Stats**
and press **L1** **ENTER**. The sample standard deviation is Sx, 5.089373342

```
1-Var Stats
 x̄=33.72916667
 Σx=809.5
 Σx²=27899.5
 Sx=5.089373342
 σx=4.982216639
↓n=24
```

◀

▶ **Example 9 (pg. 78)** Standard Deviation of Grouped Data

Press **STAT** and select **1:Edit**. Clear **L1** and **L2**. Enter the x-values into **L1**
and the frequencies into **L2**. Press **STAT** and highlight **CALC** to select the Calc
Menu. Select **1:1-Var Stats** and press **ENTER**. Type in **L1** ⌐ **L2** and press
ENTER. From the statistics displayed, the mean is 1.82 and the sample standard
deviation is 1.722.

```
1-Var Stats
 x̄=1.82
 Σx=91
 Σx²=311
 Sx=1.722480414
 σx=1.705168613
↓n=50
```

◀

▶ Exercise 17 (pg. 81) Comparing Two Datasets

Press **STAT** and select **1:Edit**. Clear **L1** and **L2**. Enter the Los Angeles Data into **L1** and the Long Beach Data into **L2**. Press **STAT** and highlight **CALC**. Select **1:1-Var Stats** and press **L1** **ENTER**. The sample standard deviation for the Los Angeles data is Sx = 6.111.

```
1-Var Stats
 x̄=26.25555556
 Σx=236.3
 Σx²=6502.97
 Sx=6.111282826
 σx=5.761772704
↓n=9
■
```

To find the range, scroll down through the display and find **minX = 18.3**. Continue scrolling through the display and find **maxX = 35.9**. To calculate the range, simply type in **35.9 - 18.3** and press **ENTER**. The range = 17.6.

```
minX=18.3
Q₁=20.55
Med=26.1
Q₃=31.85
maxX=35.9
35.9-18.3
            17.6
```

To find the variance, you must square the standard deviation. Type in 6.111 and press the x^2 key. The variance is 37.344.

```
Med=26.1
 Q₃=31.85
 maxX=35.9
35.9-18.3
            17.6
6.111²
     37.344321
```

For the Long Beach Data, press **STAT** , highlight **CALC**, select **1:1-Var Stats**, press **ENTER** and press 2nd **L2.**

```
1-Var Stats L2█
```

Press **ENTER**. The sample standard deviation for the Long Beach Data is Sx = 2.952.

```
1-Var Stats
 x̄=22.87777778
 Σx=205.9
 Σx²=4780.25
 Sx=2.952023788
 σx=2.783194718
↓n=9
█
```

Use the same procedure as you used for the Los Angeles Data, to find the range and the variance for the Long Beach Data.

◀

Section 2.5

▸ Example 2 (pg. 88) Finding Quartiles

Press **STAT** and select **1:Edit**. Clear **L1** and enter the data into **L1**. Press
STAT and highlight **CALC**. Select **1:1-Var Stats** and press **L1 ENTER**.
Scroll down through the descriptive statistics. You will see the first quartile, **Q1**
= 21.5, the second quartile (the median), **Med = 23** and the third quartile, **Q3 =
28.**

```
1-Var Stats
↑n=25
 minX=15
 Q₁=21.5
 Med=23
 Q₃=28
 maxX=30
```

◀

▶ Example 4 (pg. 90) Drawing a Box-and-Whisker-Plot

Press **STAT** and select **1:Edit**. Clear **L1** and enter the data from Example 1 on pg. 87 in your textbook. Press **2ⁿᵈ** [STAT PLOT]. Select **1:Plot 1** and press **ENTER**. Turn On **Plot 1**. Using the right arrow (you can not use the down arrow to drop to the second line), scroll through the **Type** options and choose the second boxplot which is the middle entry in row 2 of the **TYPE** options. Press **ENTER**. Move to **Xlist** and type in **L1**. Press **ENTER** and move to **Freq**. Set **Freq** to **1**. If **Freq** is set on **L2**, press **CLEAR**, and press **ALPHA** to return the cursor to a flashing solid rectangle and type in 1. Press **ZOOM** and **9** to select **ZoomStat**. The Boxplot will appear on your screen.

If you press **TRACE** and use the left and right arrow keys, you can display the five values that represent the five-number summary of the data.

Notice in the above screen display that the trace cursor is on the right side of the box, which represents the third quartile. Also, at the bottom of the screen it is noted that Q3=18.

▸ Exercise 1 (pg. 93) Quartiles and a Box-and-Whisker-Plot

Press **STAT** and select **1:Edit**. Clear **L1** and enter the data . Press **2ⁿᵈ** [STAT PLOT]. Select **1:Plot 1** and press **ENTER**. Turn On **Plot 1**. Using the right arrow, scroll through the **Type** options and choose the second boxplot which is the second entry in row 2 of the **TYPE** options. Press **ENTER**. Move to **Xlist** and type in **L1**. Press **ENTER** and move to **Freq**. Set **Freq** to **1**. If **Freq** is set on **L2**, press **CLEAR** , and press **ALPHA** to return the cursor to a flashing solid rectangle and type in **1**. Press **ZOOM** and 9 to select **ZoomStat.** The Boxplot will appear on your screen. If you press **TRACE** and use the right and left arrows, you can display **Q1, Med** and **Q3**. Notice Med=6 for this example.

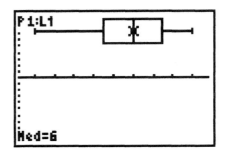

◀

> **▶ Exercise 17 (pg. 94)** Quartiles and a Box-and-Whisker-Plot

Press **STAT** and select **1:Edit**. Clear **L1** and enter the data. Press **2nd** [STAT PLOT]. Select **1:Plot 1** and press **ENTER**. Turn **On Plot 1**. Using the right arrow, scroll through the **Type** options and choose the second boxplot which is the second entry in row 2 of the **TYPE** options. Press **ENTER**. Move to **Xlist** and type in **L1**. Press **ENTER** and move to **Freq**. Set **Freq** to 1. If **Freq** is set on **L2**, press **CLEAR**, and press **ALPHA** to return the cursor to a flashing solid rectangle and type in 1. Press **ZOOM** and **9** to select **ZoomStat.** The Boxplot will appear on your screen. If you press **TRACE** and use the right and left arrows, you can display **Q1, Med** and **Q3**.

Using the quartiles and the Boxplot, you can make several statements about the data. Here are a few suggestions:

25% of the individuals in the sample watch less than 2 hours of television per day.

25% of the individuals in the sample watch more than 5 hours of television per day.

50% of the individuals in the sample watch between 2 and 5 hours of television per day.

Because the right whisker is somewhat longer than the left whisker, the data appears slightly skewed to the right.

◀

▶ Technology Lab (pg. 97) Monthly Milk Production

Exercises 1-2: Press **STAT** and select **1:Edit**. Clear **L1** and enter the data into **L1**. Press **STAT** and highlight **CALC**. Select **1:1-Var Stats** and press **L1** **ENTER**. The sample mean and sample standard deviation can be found in the output display.

Exercises 3-4. You will use the histogram of the data to construct the frequency distribution. To construct a histogram, press 2nd [STAT PLOT]. Select **1: Plot 1** and **ENTER**. Turn ON **Plot 1** by highlighting **On** and pressing **ENTER**. Scroll through the **Type** icons, highlight the **Histogram** and press **ENTER**. Move to **Xlist** and type in **L1.** Move to the **Freq** entry and type in **1.** (Note: If the Freq entry is **L2**, Press **CLEAR** , press **ALPHA** and enter **1**). To view a histogram of the data, press **ZOOM** and **9**. To adjust the histogram, press **Window**. Set **Xmin = 1000** and set **Xscl = 500**. (All other entries in the Window Menu can remain unchanged). Press **GRAPH** and then press **TRACE**.

The minimum and maximum values of the first category are displayed. (**1000 and < 1500**). The midpoint of the first category is (1000+1499)/2, which is **1249.5.** The frequency for the first category is **n = 6.** Trace through the histogram and set up a frequency distribution for the data:

Category	Midpoint	Frequency
1000 – 1499	1249.5	6

Exercise 5. Using the values that you found in Exercises 1 and 2, calculate the lower and upper endpoints of the one and two standard deviation intervals: $(\bar{x} \pm 1s)$ and $(\bar{x} \pm 2s)$. Next, press 2nd [LIST]. Highlight **OPS** and select **1:SortA(** , press **ENTER**. Press 2nd [L1] and close the parentheses. Press

ENTER. Press STAT, select **1:Edit** and press ENTER. Scroll through the data in **L1** and count the number of data points that fall in the one and two standard deviation intervals: $(\bar{x} \pm 1s)$ and $(\bar{x} \pm 2s)$. To find the percentage of data points that lie in each of these intervals, calculate: (number of data points in each interval/ 50) * 100. Compare these percentages with the percentages stated in the Empirical rule.

Exercises 6 - 7. Using the frequency distribution you created, enter the midpoints into **L2** and the frequencies into **L3**. Press STAT , highlight **CALC**. Select **1:1-Var Stats** and press ENTER. Type in **L2** , **L3** and press ENTER. The mean and standard deviation for the frequency distribution will be displayed on the screen.

Exercise 8: Compare the actual values for the mean and standard deviation that you found in Exercises 1 and 2 to the estimates for the mean and standard deviation that you found in Exercises 6 and 7.

CHAPTER

3

Probability

Section 3.1

▶ Law of Large Numbers (pg. 114)

You can use the TI-83 to simulate tossing a coin 500 times. In this simulation, we will designate "0" as Heads and "1" as Tails.

Press **MATH**, highlight **PRB**, and select **5:randInt(** and press **ENTER**. The **randInt(** command requires a minimum value, (which is 0 for this simulation), a maximum value (which is 1), and the number of trials (500). In the **randInt(** command type in **0** $\boxed{,}$ **1** $\boxed{,}$ **500.**

```
randInt(0,1,500)
```

Press **ENTER**. It will take several seconds for the calculator to generate 500 tosses. Notice, in the upper right hand corner a flashing $\boxed{\ |\ }$, indicating that the calculator is working. When the simulation has been completed, a string of **0's** and **1's** will appear on the screen followed by **....,** indicating that there are more numbers in the string that are not shown.

Press **STO** and 2nd **[L1]**   **ENTER** . This will store the string of numbers in **L1**.
Press 2nd **[LIST]** and highlight **MATH**. Select **sum(** and type in **L1**.

The sum of **L1** equals the number of Tails in the list. For this particular
simulation, the sum is 242. The number of Heads is equal to (500 - no. of Tails).
The proportion of Heads is (no. of Heads / 999). How close is this proportion to
50% ?

Section 3.2

▶ **Exercise 26d (pg.129)** Birthday Problem

To simulate this problem, press MATH, highlight **PRB**, select **5:randInt(** and
enter **1** ⎡,⎤ **365** ⎡,⎤ **24.**

```
randInt(1,365,24
)
{250 364 159 26…
```

Store the data in **L1** by pressing STO and 2nd **[L1]** ENTER. To see if there are
at least two people with the same birthday, you must look for a matching pair of
numbers in **L1**. To do this, press 2nd **[LIST]**, highlight **OPS** and select **1:SortA(**
and press ENTER. The column you want to sort in ascending order is **L1**, so type
2nd **[L1]** into the sort command and press ENTER.

```
randInt(1,365,24
)
{292 351 153 60…
Ans→L1
{292 351 153 60…
SortA(L1)
            Done
```

Press STAT and select **1:EDIT**, press ENTER and scroll down through **L1** and
check for matching numbers. If you find any matching numbers, that means that
at least 2 people in your simulation have the same birthday.

```
┌──────┬──────┬──────────┐
│ L1   │ L2   │ L3     1 │
├──────┼──────┼──────────┤
│ 15   │──────│──────    │
│ 15   │      │          │
│ 23   │      │          │
│ 44   │      │          │
│ 60   │      │          │
│ 64   │      │          │
│ 74   │      │          │
├──────┴──────┴──────────┤
│ L1(1)=15               │
└────────────────────────┘
```

Notice in this simulation, 15 is listed twice. This represents two people with the same birthday, January 15 (the 15th day of a year). That means that for your first simulation you have found at least two people with the same birthday. Since you have found this matching pair right at the beginning of **L1**, you do not need to look further into the data in **L1**. Repeat this simulation process nine more times, each time checking to see if you have a matching pair.

How many of your simulations resulted in at least one matching pair? Suppose you found a matching pair in 5 out of your 10 simulations. That means that your estimate of the probability of finding at least 2 people with the same birthday in a room of 24 people is "5 out of 10" or 50%.

◀

Section 3.4

▶ **Example 3 (pg. 142)** Finding the Number of Permutations

You have a baseball team consisting of nine players. To find the number of different batting orders that are possible, you must calculate the number of permutations of **9** objects taken **9** at a time. The formula **nPr** is used with **n = 9** (the number of players on the team) and **r = 9** (the number of players you will be selecting). So, the formula is **9P9**.

Press █, MATH, highlight **PRB** and select **2:nPr** and ENTER.

Now press █ and ENTER. The answer, 362880, appears on the screen.

▶ Example 5 (pg. 143) More Permutations

Use the permutation formula with **n = 43** and **r = 3**. Enter **43,** press MATH, highlight **PRB**, select **2:nPr** and press ENTER. Now enter 3 and press ENTER.

▶ Example 6 (pg. 144) Distinguishable Permutations

To calculate $\dfrac{12!}{6!4!2!}$ you will use the factorial function (**!**). Enter the first value, **12,** press MATH, highlight **PRB** and select **4:!** . Then press ÷ . Open the parentheses by pressing (. Enter the next value, **6,** press MATH, **PRB**, and select **4:!** . To multiply by 4!, press × and enter the next value, **4.** Press MATH, **PRB**, and select **4:!** . To multiply by 2!, press × and enter the next value, **2.** Press MATH, **PRB**, and select **4:!** . Close the parentheses) and press ENTER.

▶ Example 7 (pg. 145) Finding the Number of Combinations

To calculate the number of different combinations of four companies that can be selected from 16 bidding companies you will use the combination formula: **nCr,** where n = the total number of items in the group and r = the number of items being selected. In this example, the formula is **16C4.** Enter the first value, **16,** press MATH, highlight **PRB** and select **3: nCr,** and enter the second value, **4.** Press ENTER and the answer will be displayed on the screen..

```
16 nCr 4
              1820
```

▶ Example 9 (pg. 146) Finding Probabilities

To calculate the probability of being dealt five diamonds from a standard deck of 52 playing cards, you must calculate: $\dfrac{13C5}{52C5}$.

To calculate the numerator, enter the first value, **13,** press MATH, highlight **PRB** and select **3:nCr** and enter the next value, **5.** Next press ÷ and enter the first value in the denominator, **52,** press MATH, highlight **PRB** and select **3:nCr,** enter the next value, **5.** Press ENTER and the answer will be displayed on your screen.

```
13 nCr 5/52 nCr
5
   4.951980792E-4
```

Notice that the answer is written in scientific notation. To convert to standard notation, move the decimal point 4 places to the left. Thus, the answer is .000495.

▸ Exercise 34 (pg. 149) Probability

a. To calculate **200C15**, enter the first value, **200**, press MATH, highlight **PRB** and select **3:nCr**, enter the next value, **15** and press ENTER.

b. Calculate **144C15** (follow the steps for part a.).

c. The probability that *no* minorities are selected is equal to the probability that the committee is composed completely of non-minorities. This probability can be calculated with the following formula: $\dfrac{144C15}{200C15}$.

(Use the answer from part b for the numerator and the answer from part a for the denominator.)

◂

▶ Technology Lab (pg. 151) Composing Mozart Variations

Exercises 3 - 4: To select one number from 1 to 11, press MATH, highlight **PRB** and select **5:randInt(** and enter **1** |,| **11**) and press ENTER. One random number between 1 and 11 will be displayed on the screen.

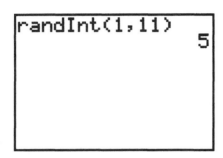

3a. Hint: Each number from 1 to 11 has an equal chance of being selected. So each of the 11 possibilities has equal probability. What is this theoretical probability? (Use this to answer the question in Exercise 4.)

3b. To select 100 integers between 1 and 11, press MATH, highlight **PRB** and select **5:randInt(** and enter **1** |,| **11** |,| **100**) and press ENTER. Store the results in L1 by pressing STO, 2nd **[L1]**, ENTER. Next you can create a histogram and use it to tally your results. **To create the histogram, press** 2nd [STAT PLOT], select **1:Plot 1** and press ENTER. Turn **ON** Plot 1, set **Type** to **Histogram.** Set **Xlist** to **L1** and **Freq** to **1.** Press ZOOM and select 9 for **ZoomStat.** Press WINDOW and set **Xscl** = **1,** then press GRAPH. Use TRACE to scroll through the bars of the histogram.

The first bar represents the number of times that a "**1**" occurred in the 100 tosses. (Notice on the screen: min = 1and n=9). Use the right arrow to scroll through the bars in the histogram. As the cursor moves from one bar in the histogram to the next bar, the "min =" will indicate the current x-value and the "n=" will indicate the corresponding frequency. Record the x-values and the corresponding frequencies in a table. For example, using the histogram in the above diagram, the frequency table would begin with X = 1, n = 9. Convert each frequency into a relative frequency by dividing each frequency by 100, and use the relative frequencies to answer the question in Exercise 4.

Exercise 5: To select 2 random numbers from 1 to 6, press MATH, highlight **PRB** and select **5:randInt(** and enter **1** [,] **6** [,] **2**) and press ENTER. Add the two numbers in the display and subtract **1** from the total.

5a.   First list all possible pairs. (There are 36 pairs: (1,1), (1,2), (1,3)....). For each pair, find the sum and subtract "1" to find a total. Make a frequency table listing all the possible totals from 1 to 11. Next to each total record the number of times that total occurred. Lastly, convert each of these frequencies to relative frequencies by dividing by 36. These relative frequencies are the theoretical probabilities. Use them to answer the question in Exercise 6.

5b. To select 100 totals, create 2 columns of 100 random numbers. Press MATH, highlight **PRB** and select **5:randInt(** and enter **1** [,] **6** [,] **100**) and press ENTER. Press STO 2nd **[L1]** and ENTER to store this first string of numbers in **L1**. Next create a second set of 100 numbers using the same procedure. Press STO 2nd **[L2]** and ENTER to store this second string of numbers in **L2**. Now you can calculate the sum of each row and subtract **1**. Press STAT and select **1:EDIT**. Move the cursor to highlight **L3**.

L1	L2	3
1	4	------
3	2	
6	4	
2	3	
1	1	
1	2	
3	6	
L3 =		

Press ENTER and the cursor will move to the bottom of the screen. On the bottom line next to **L3** =, type in 2nd **[L1]** + 2nd **[L2]** - 1 and press ENTER. The results should appear in **L3.**

```
L1      L2      L3      3
1       4       4
3       2       4
6       4       9
2       3       4
1       1       1
1       2       2
3       6       8
L3(1)=4
```

Create a histogram of **L3** and use it to tally your results (follow the steps in Exercises 3 - 4 to create the histogram). Use ▮RACE▮ to find the frequencies for each X-value and record your results in a frequency table. Convert each frequency to a relative frequency and use the relative frequencies to answer the question in Exercise 6.

To create a minuet using Mozart's Musical Dice Game, simulate the tossing of 2 dice 16 times. (Press ▮MATH▮, highlight **PRB** and select **5:randInt(** and enter **1** ▮**,**▮ **6** ▮**,**▮ **16**). Store the 16 tosses of the first die in **L1** and the 16 tosses of the second die in **L2**. Calculate the sum of each row and store the sums in **L3**.

```
L1      L2      L3      3
2       1       3
3       6       9
5       4       9
6       4       10
4       3       7
5       4       9
5       1       6
L3(1)=3
```

Scroll down to the eighth item in **L3**. If this number is odd, select Option 1 for the eighth bar of the minuet. If it is even, select Option2 for the eighth bar.

```
L1      L2      L3      3
3       6       9
5       4       9
6       4       10
4       3       7
5       4       9
5       1       6
3       5       8
L3(8) =8
```

In this example, the eighth item in **L3** is **8**, so the eighth bar of the minuet is Option2. Next, scroll down to the sixteenth item in **L3**. If this number is odd, select Option 1 for the sixteenth bar of the minuet. If it is even, select Option2 for the sixteenth bar.

L1	L2	L3	3
2	6	8	
3	6	9	
1	1	2	
2	3	5	
4	1	5	
6	2	8	
5	6	11	

L3(16) = 11

In this example, the sixteenth item in **L3** is 11, so the sixteenth bar of the minuet is Option1.

For each of the other bars in the minuet, subtract **1** from the total. To do this, highlight **L3.** Press ENTER. On the bottom line of the screen, next to **L3** = type in **L3 - 1.** Press ENTER and the new values in **L3** will be displayed on the screen.

L1	L2	L3	3
2	1	2	
3	6	8	
5	4	8	
6	4	9	
4	3	6	
5	4	8	
5	1	5	

L3(1) = 2

The first 7 numbers in **L3** represent the first 7 bars of the minuet. Items 9 through 15 in **L3** represent the 9th through 15th bars of the minuet. Combine these values with bars **8** and **16** that you previously selected and you have the completed minuet. In this example, the resulting minuet is: 2 8 8 9 6 8 5 2 10 7 8 1 4 4 7 1.

◀

Discrete Probability Distributions

CHAPTER

4

Section 4.1

▶ Example 5 (pg. 166) Mean of a Probability Distribution

Press **STAT** and select **1:EDIT**. Clear **L1** and **L2**. Enter the X-values into **L1** and the P(x) values into **L2**. Press **STAT** and highlight **CALC**. Select **1:1-Var Stats,** press **ENTER** and press 2nd [L1] , 2nd [L2] **ENTER** to see the descriptive statistics. The mean score is 2.94.

```
1-Var Stats
 x̄=2.94
 Σx=2.94
 Σx²=10.26
 Sx=
 σx=1.271377206
↓n=1
```

◀

▶ Example 6 (pg. 167) The Variance and Standard Deviation

Using the data from Example 5 on pg. 166, which you stored in **L1** and **L2**, press
STAT highlight **CALC**. Select **1:1-Var Stats,** press ENTER and press 2nd [L1]
, 2nd **[L2]** ENTER. The population standard deviation , σx, is 1.27.

```
1-Var Stats
 x̄=2.94
 Σx=2.94
 Σx²=10.26
 Sx=
 σx=1.271377206
↓n=1
█
```

To find the variance, you must use the value of the standard deviation. Since the
variance is equal to the standard deviation squared, type in **1.2714** and press the
x^2 key. The population variance is **1.616**.

```
 Σx=2.94
 Σx²=10.26
 Sx=
 σx=1.271377206
↓n=1
1.2714²
          1.61645796
```

◀

Section 4.2

▶ Example 5 (pg. 179) Binomial Probabilities

To find a binomial probability you will use the binomial probability density function, **binompdf(n,p,x).** For this example, n = 100, p = .58 and x = 65. Press 2nd **[DISTR]**. Scroll down through the menu to select **0:binompdf(** and press **ENTER** . Type in **100** ⎵ **.58** ⎵ **65**) and press **ENTER**. The answer, **.0299**, will appear on the screen.

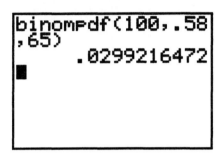

◀

▶ Example 6 (pg. 180) Binomial Probabilities

For this example, n = 4 and p = .41. You want to calculate P(X = 2), P(X ≥ 2) and P(X < 2). Since n is a small number, you can easily display the individual probabilities for each X-value (X = 0,1,2,3,4). To make it easier to view the individual probabilities, change the number of decimal places in the display by pressing MODE and changing **FLOAT** (on line 2 of the display) to **3**.

Press ENTER. This will round each of the probabilities to 3 decimal places. Press 2nd **[QUIT]**.

To calculate the individual probabilities, you will use the command: **binompdf(n,p,x).** If you do not enter a value for **x** in this command, the probabilities for all possible X-values will be calculated and displayed on the screen. So, press 2nd **[DISTR]** and select **0:binompdf(**   and type in **4** , **.41**) and press ENTER. The output is (**.121, .337, .351, .163, .028).** Use the right arrow to scroll through the output. These probabilities are P(X = 0), P(X = 1), P(X = 2), P(X = 3), and P(X = 4). To find P(X ≥ 2) simply add .351 + .163 + .028.

▶ Example 7 (pg. 181) Graphing Binomial Distributions

Construct a probability distribution for a binomial probability model with n = 6 and p = .65. Press STAT, select **1:EDIT** and clear **L1** and **L2**. Enter the values 0 through 6 into **L1**. Press 2nd [QUIT]. To calculate the probabilities for each X-value in **L1**, first change the display mode so that the probabilities displayed will be rounded to 3 decimal places. Press MODE and change from **FLOAT** to **3** and press 2nd [QUIT]. Next press 2nd [DISTR] and select **0:binompdf(** and type in **6** , .65) and press ENTER. Store these probabilities in **L2** by pressing STO 2nd [L2] ENTER.

```
binompdf(6,.65)
{.002 .020 .095…
Ans→L₂
{.002 .020 .095…
```

To graph the binomial distribution, press 2nd [STAT PLOT] and press ENTER. Turn **ON** Plot 1, select **Histogram** for **Type**, type in 2nd [L1] for **Xlist** and 2nd [L2] for **Freq**. Press ZOOM and select 9 for **ZoomStat**. Adjust the graph by pressing WINDOW and setting **Xmin = 0, Xmax = 7, Xscl = 1, Ymin = 0** and **Ymax = .35**. Choosing an Xmax=7, leaves some space at the right of the graph in order to complete the histogram. The Ymax value was selected by looking through the values in **L2** and then rounding the largest value UP to a convenient number. Press GRAPH to view the histogram.

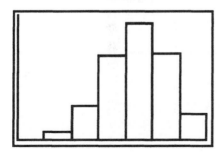

▶ Exercise 9 (pg. 184) Binomial Probabilities

A multiple-choice quiz consists of five questions and each question has four possible answers. If you randomly guess the answer to each question, the probability of getting the correct answer is 1 in 4, so p = .25 and n = 5.

a. To calculate P(x = 3), press 2nd [DISTR] and select **0:binompdf(** and type in 5 ⌐,⌐ .25 ⌐,⌐ 3 ⌐)⌐ and press ENTER.

b-c. To calculate inequalities, such as P(X ≥ 3) or P(X < 3) , you can use the cumulative probability command: **binomcdf (n,p,x)**. This command accumulates probability starting at X = 0 and ending at a specified X-value. To calculate the probability of guessing at least three answers correctly, that is P(X ≥ 3), press 2nd [DISTR] and select **A:binomcdf(** by scrolling through the options and selecting **A:binomcdf(** or by pressing ALPHA A. (Note: A is the ALPHA function on the MATH key.) Type in 5 ⌐,⌐ .25 ⌐,⌐ 2 ⌐)⌐ and press ENTER. The result, P(X ≤ 2) = .896.

```
binomcdf(5,.25,2
)
              .896
```

This result is the accumulated probability that X = 0,1 or 2, since this command, **binomcdf**, accumulates probability starting at X = 0. You want P(X ≥ 3) and this is the *complement* of P(X ≤ 2). So P(X ≥ 3) = 1 - P(X ≤ 2) which is .104. The probability of guessing *less than* 3 answers correctly is P(X ≤ 2) which equals 0.896.

◀

Section 4.3

▶ Example 1 (pg. 188) The Geometric Distribution

Suppose the probability that you will make a sale on any given telephone call is 0.23. To find the probability that your *first* sale on any given day will occur on your fourth or fifth telephone call of the day, press 2nd [DISTR] and select **D:geometpdf(** and type in **.23** ⎡,⎤ 2nd ⎡{⎤ **4** ⎡,⎤ **5** 2nd ⎡}⎤ ⎡)⎤. This command will display 2 probabilites: P(X = 4) and P(X = 5). The probability that your first sale of the day will occur on your fourth or fifth sales call of the day is .105003 + .080852.

▶ Example 2 (pg. 189) The Poisson Distribution

Use the command **poissonpdf (μ,x)** with μ = 3 and x = 4. Press 2nd [DISTR] and select **B:poissonpdf(** and type in **3** ⎡,⎤ **4** ⎡)⎤ and press ENTER. The answer will appear on the screen.

```
poissonpdf(3,4)
        .1680313557
```

▶ Exercise 11 (pg. 193) Poisson Distribution

This is a Poisson probability problem with $\mu = 8$.

a.   To find the probability that exactly 4 businesses will fail in any given hour, press 2nd [DISTR] and select **B:poissonpdf(** . Type in **8** $\boxed{,}$ **4** $\boxed{)}$ and press ENTER.

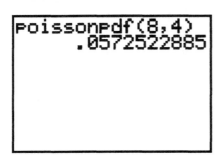

b.   Use the cumulative probability command **poissoncdf(.** This command accumulates probability starting at $X = 0$ and ending at the specified X-value. To calculate the probability that at least 4 businesses will fail in any given hour, that is $P(X \geq 4)$, you must find $P(X \leq 3)$ and subtract from 1. Press 2nd [DISTR] , select **C:poissoncdf(** and type in **8** $\boxed{,}$ **3** $\boxed{)}$ and press ENTER. The result, $P(X \leq 3)$, is .0424. This result is the accumulated probability that $X = 0,1,2,$ or 3. $P(X \geq 4)$ is the *complement* of $P(X \leq 3)$. So, $P(X \geq 4)$ is 1 - .0424 or .9576.

c.   To find the probability that more than 4 businesses will fail in any given hour, find $P(X > 4)$. So, first calculate the *complement*, $P(X \leq 4)$, and then subtract the answer from 1.

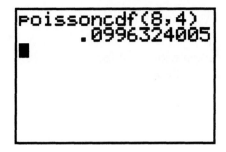

▶ Technology Lab (pg. 195)

Exercise 1: Create a Poisson probability distribution with $\mu = 4$ for $X = 0$ to 20.
Press STAT and select **1:EDIT** . Clear **L1** and **L2**. Enter the integers
0,1,2,3,...20 into **L1** and press 2nd **[QUIT]**.

For this example, it is helpful to display the probabilities with 3 decimal places.
Press MODE. Move the cursor to the 2nd line and select **3** and press ENTER.

Press 2nd **[DISTR]** and select **B:poissonpdf(** . Type in **4** ⌐ 2nd **[L1]** and press
ENTER .

```
PoissonPdf(4,L1)
{.018 .073 .147…
■
```

A partial display of the probabilities will appear. Press STO and 2nd **[L2]**
ENTER. Press STAT, and select **1:EDIT.** **L1** and **L2** will be displayed on the
screen.

L1	L2	L3	1
0.0000	.018	------	
1.000	.073		
2.000	.147		
3.000	.195		
4.000	.195		
5.000	.156		
6.000	.104		
L1(1)=0			

Notice that the X-values in **L1** now have 3 decimal places. This is a result of
setting the MODE to **3.** Each value in **L2** is the poisson probability associated
with the X-value in **L1**. So, for example, $P(X = 2)$ is .147. Scroll through **L2** and
compare the probabilities in **L2** with the heights if the corresponding bars in the
frequency histogram on page 195.

Exercises 3 - 5: Use another technology tool to generate the random numbers. The TI-83 cannot generate poisson random data.

Exercise 6: For this exercise, $\mu = 5$ and $X = 10$. Press 2nd **[DISTR]** and select **B:poissonpdf(** . Type in **5** ⎵ **10** and press ENTER .

Exercise 7: Use the probability distribution that you generated in Exercise 1.

a.   Sum the probabilities in **L2** that correspond to X- values of 3, 4 and 5 in **L1**.

b.   Sum the probabilities in **L2** that correspond to X- values of 0,1,2,3 and 4 in **L1**. This is $P(X \leq 4)$. Subtract this sum from **1** to get $P(X > 4)$.

c.   Assuming that the number of arrivals per minute are independent events, raise $P(X > 4)$ to the fourth power.

Normal Probability Distributions

Section 5.3

▶ **Example 3 (pg. 224)** Normal Probabilities

Suppose that cholesterol levels of American men are normally distributed with a mean of 215 and a standard deviation of 25. If you randomly select one American male, calculate the probability that his cholesterol is less than 175, that is P(X < 175).

The TI-83 has two methods for calculating this probability.

Method 1: **Normalcdf(**lowerbound, upperbound, μ, σ) computes probability between a lowerbound and an upperbound. In this example, you are computing the probability from negative infinity to 175. Negative infinity is specified by [-] 1 2nd **[EE]** 9 9 (Note: **EE** is found above the comma ,). Try entering −1 EE 99 into your calculator.

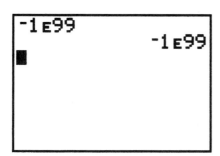

Now, to calculate P(X < 175), press 2nd **[DISTR]** and select **2:normalcdf(** and type in **-1E99** , **175** , **215** , **25** **)** and press ENTER.

Technical note: Theoretically, the normal probability distribution (the bell-shaped curve) extends infinitely to the right and left of the mean (see Textbook pg. 206). In this particular problem, P(X < 175), you do not necessarily have to use negative infinity (-1 EE 99) as your lowerbound. If you look at this example in your textbook on pg. 224, the lowerbound is set at 0. This is a perfectly fine selection since no individual will have a cholesterol level less than 0.

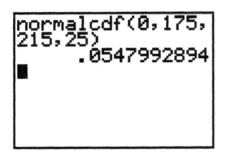

Notice that your results are the same in both of the above screens.

Method 2: This method calculates P(X < 175) and also displays a graph of the probability distribution. You must first set up the WINDOW so that the graph will be displayed properly. You will need to set Xmin equal to (μ - 3 σ) and Xmax equal to (μ + 3 σ). Press WINDOW and set **Xmin** equal to (μ - 3 σ) by entering **215 - 3 * 25.** Press ENTER and set **Xmax** equal to (μ + 3 σ) by entering **215 + 3 * 25.** Set **Xscl** equal to σ.

 Setting the Y-range is a little more difficult to do. A good "rule - of - thumb" is to set **Ymax** equal to .5 / σ. For this example, type in **.5 / 25** for **Ymax.**

```
WINDOW
 Xmin=140
 Xmax=290
 Xscl=25
 Ymin=-.005
 Ymax=.5/25█
 Yscl=1
 Xres=1
```

Use the blue up arrow to highlight **Ymin**. A good value for **Ymin** is **(-) Ymax / 4**
so type in [(-)] **.02 / 4**.

```
WINDOW
 Xmin=140
 Xmax=290
 Xscl=25
 Ymin=-.02/4█
 Ymax=.02
 Yscl=1
 Xres=1
```

Press 2nd [QUIT]. Clear all the previous drawings by pressing 2nd **[DRAW]**
and selecting **1:ClrDraw** and pressing ENTER ENTER. Now you can draw the
probability distribution. Press 2nd **[DISTR]**. Highlight **DRAW** and select
1:ShadeNorm(and type in -1E99 ⌐ 175 ⌐ 215 ⌐ 25 ⌐ and press ENTER. The
output displays a normal curve with the appropriate area shaded in and its value
computed.

▶ Exercise 7 (pg. 225) Finding Probabilities

In this exercise, use a normal distribution with $\mu = 69.2$ and $\sigma = 2.9$.

Method 1:To find P(X < 66), press 2nd [DISTR] , select **2:normalcdf(** and type in **-1E99** $\boxed{,}$ **66** $\boxed{,}$ **69.2** $\boxed{,}$ **2.9** $\boxed{)}$ and press ENTER. (Note: Since no male will have a height less than 0 inches, you could have used "0" in place of -1 EE 99 as your lowerbound.

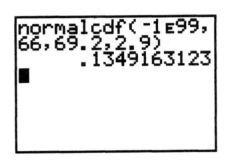

Method 2: To find P(X < 66) and include a graph, you must first set up the Graph Window. Press WINDOW and set **Xmin = 69.2 - 3 * 2.9 and Xmax = 69.2 + 3 * 2.9**. Set **Xscl** = 2.9. Set **Ymax = .5 / 2.9) and Ymin =** **-.1724/4.** Press 2nd [DRAW] and select **1:ClrDraw** and press ENTER ENTER. Press 2nd [DISTR], highlight **DRAW** and select **1:ShadeNorm(** and type in **-1E99** $\boxed{,}$ **66** $\boxed{,}$ **69.2** $\boxed{,}$ **2.9** $\boxed{)}$ and press ENTER.

To find p(66<x< 72), press 2nd [DISTR] , select **2:normalcdf(** and type in **66** $\boxed{,}$ **72** $\boxed{,}$ **69.2** $\boxed{,}$ **2.9** $\boxed{)}$ and press ENTER .

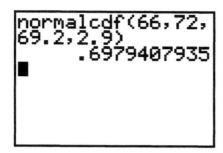

or press 2nd [DRAW] and select **1:ClrDraw** and press ENTER ENTER. Press 2nd [DISTR] , highlight **DRAW** and select **1:ShadeNorm(** and type in **66** ⎡,⎤ **72** ⎡,⎤ **69.2** ⎡,⎤ **2.9** ⎡)⎤ and press ENTER .

To find P(X > 72), press 2nd [DISTR] , select **2:normalcdf(** and type in **72** ⎡,⎤ **1E99** ⎡,⎤ **69.2** ⎡,⎤ **2.9** ⎡)⎤ and press ENTER. (Note: In this example, the lowerbound is 72 and the upperbound is positive infinity).

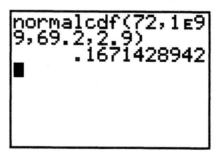

or press 2nd [DRAW] and select **1:ClrDraw** and press ENTER ENTER. Press 2nd [DISTR] , highlight **DRAW** and select **1:ShadeNorm(** and type in **72** ⎡,⎤ **1E99** ⎡,⎤ **69.2** ⎡,⎤ **2.9** ⎡)⎤ and press ENTER.

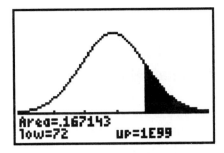

Note: When using the TI-83 (or any other technology tool), the answers you obtain may vary slightly from the answers that you would obtain using the standard normal table. Consequently, your answers may not be exactly the same as the answers found in the answer key in your textbook. The differences are simply due to rounding.

◀

Section 5.4

▶ **Example 4 (pg. 232)** Finding a Specific Data Value

This is called an inverse normal problem and the command **invNorm(area,** μ **,** σ **)** is used. In this type of problem, a percentage of the area under the normal curve is given and you are asked to find the corresponding X-value. In this example, the percentage given is the top 5 %. The TI-83 always calculates probability from negative infinity up to the specified X-value. To find the X-value corresponding to the top 5 %, you must accumulate the bottom 95 % of the area. Press **2**[nd] **[DISTR]** and select **3:invNorm(** and type in **.95** [,] **75** [,] **6.5**) and press ENTER.

```
invNorm(.95,75,6
.5)
        85.69154857
```

In order to score in the top 5 %, you must earn a score of at least 85.69. Assuming that scores are given as whole numbers, your score must be at least 86.

◀

▶ Exercise 36 (pg. 235) Heights of Males

This is the normal distribution with $\mu = 69.2$ and $\sigma = 2.9$ from Exercise 7 on pg. 225.

a. To find the 90th percentile, press **2nd** **[DISTR]** and select **3:invNorm(** and type in **.90** ⎡,⎤ **69.2** ⎡,⎤ **2.9** ⎡)⎤ and press **ENTER**.

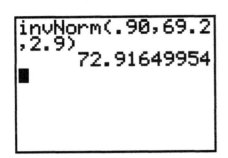

```
invNorm(.90,69.2
,2.9)
       72.91649954
█
```

b. To find the first quartile, press **2nd** **[DISTR]** and select **3:invNorm(** and type in **.25** ⎡,⎤ **69.2** ⎡,⎤ **2.9** ⎡)⎤ and press **ENTER** .

```
invNorm(.25,69.2
,2.9)
      67.24397973
█
```

◀

Section 5.5

▶ **Example 4 (pg. 243)** Probabilities for Sampling Distributions

In this example, a sample of n = 50 adults ages 18 to 24 is selected and the length of time each person spends reading is recorded. From the graph on pg. 243, you will find that the mean reading time for adults in the 18 to 24 age group is: $\mu = 9$ minutes. The problem states that the assumed standard deviation is $\sigma = 1.5$ minutes. Since n > 30, you can conclude that the sampling distribution of the sample mean is approximately normal with $u_{\bar{x}} = 9$ and $\sigma_{\bar{x}} = 1.5/\sqrt{50}$. To calculate P($8.7 < \bar{x} < 9.5$), press 2nd **[DISTR]** , select **2:normalcdf(** and type in **8.7** $\boxed{,}$ **9.5** $\boxed{,}$ **9** $\boxed{,}$ **1.5/$\sqrt{50}$** $\boxed{)}$ and press ENTER.

```
normalcdf(8.7,9.
5,9,1.5/√(50)
       .9121393013
```

Note: The answer in your textbook is 0.9116. This answer was calculated using the z-table. Since z-values in the table are rounded to hundredths, the answers will vary slightly from those obtained using the TI-83.

◀

▶ Example 6 (pg. 245) Finding Probabilities for x and $\bar{x}$

The population is normally distributed with $\mu = 2870$ and $\sigma = 900$.

1. To calculate P(X <2500), press 2nd [DISTR] , select **2:normalcdf(** and type in **-1E99** [,] **2500** [,] **2870** [,] **900** [ )] and press ENTER. (Note: Since the minimum credit card balance is 0, the lowerbound could be set at 0, rather than negative infinity.)

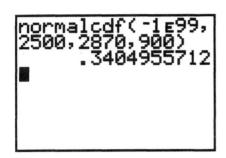

```
normalcdf(-1E99,
2500,2870,900)
         .3404955712
■
```

2. To calculate P($\bar{x}$ <2500), press 2nd [DISTR] , select **2:normalcdf(** and type in **-1E99** [,] **2500** [,] **2870** [,] **900/**$\sqrt{25}$ [ )] and press ENTER.

```
normalcdf(-1E99,
2500,2870,900/√(
25))
         .0199126205
■
```

◀

▶ Exercise 19 (pg. 248) Make a Decision

To decide whether the machine needs to be reset, you must decide how unlikely it would be to find a mean of 127.9 from a sample of 40 cans if, in fact, the machine is actually operating correctly at $\mu = 128$. One method of determining the likelihood of $\bar{x} = 127.9$ is to calculate how far 127.9 is from the mean of 128. You can do this by calculating how much area there is under the normal curve to the left of 127.9. The smaller that area is, the farther 127.9 is from the mean and the more unlikely 127.9 is.

To calculate $P(\bar{x} \leq 127.9)$, press 2nd [DISTR] , select **2:normalcdf(** and type in **-1E99** ⬚ , **127.9** ⬚ , **128** ⬚ , **0.20/$\sqrt{40}$** ⬚ and press ENTER .

Notice that the answer is displayed in scientific notation: 7.827E-4. Convert this to standard notation, .0007827, by moving the decimal point 4 places to the left. This probability is extremely small; therefore, the event ($\bar{x} \leq 127.9$) is highly unlikely if the mean is actually 128. So, something has gone wrong with the machine and the actual mean must have shifted to a value less than 128.

◀

▸ Technology Lab (pg. 250) Age Distribution in the U. S.

Exercise 1: Press STAT and select **1:EDIT**. Clear **L1, L2** and **L3**.
Enter the age distribution into **L1** and **L2** by putting class midpoints in **L1** and relative frequencies (converted to decimals) into **L2**. (The first entry is 2.5 in **L1** and .069 in **L2**.) To find the population mean, μ , and the population standard deviation, σ , press STAT, highlight **CALC**, select **1:1-Var Stats**, press ENTER and press 2nd [L1] , 2nd [L2] ENTER. The mean and the standard deviation will be displayed. (Note: Use " σ x" because the age data represents the entire population distribution of ages, not a sample.)

Exercise 2: Enter the thirty-six sample means into **L3**. To find the mean and standard deviation of these sample means, press STAT, highlight **CALC**, select **1:1-Var Stats**. Press ENTER and press 2nd [L3] ENTER. The mean and the standard deviation will be displayed. (Note: use "sx" because the 36 sample means are a sample of 36 means, not the entire population of all possible means of size n = 40).

Exercise 3: Construct a histogram of the age distribution. Press 2nd **[STAT PLOT]** and select **1: Plot** 1. Turn **ON** Plot 1, select **Histogram** for **Type,** set **Xlist** to **L1** and set **Freq** to **L2**. Press ZOOM and 9 for **ZoomStat.** Adjust the WINDOW by pressing WINDOW and setting **Xmax = 102.5, Xscl = 5, Ymin = -.02 and Ymax = .09.**

Exercise 4: The TI-83 will draw a frequency histogram, not a *relative* frequency histogram. (The shape of the data can be determined from either type of histogram). Press 2nd **[STAT PLOT]** and select **1: Plot 1. Plot 1** has already been turned **ON** and **Histogram** has been selected for **Type**. Set **Xlist** to **L3**. On the **Freq** line, press CLEAR and ALPHA to return to the standard rectangular cursor and enter 1. Press ZOOM and 9 for **ZoomStat.** To adjust the histogram so that it has nine classes, press WINDOW. Approximate the class width using (48 - 28)/9. This value is approximately 2, so set **Xscl = 2** and press GRAPH.

Exercise 5: See the output from Exercise 1 for the population standard deviation.

Exercise 6: See the output from Exercise 2 for the standard deviation of the sample means.

Confidence Intervals

Section 6.1

▶ Example 4 (pg. 274)   Constructing a Confidence Interval

Enter the data from Example 1 on pg. 270 into **L1**. In this example, n > 30, so the
sample standard deviation, Sx, is a good approximation of σ, the population
standard deviation. To find Sx, press **STAT**, highlight **CALC**, select **1:1-Var
Stats** and press **L1** **ENTER**.

The sample standard deviation is Sx = 5.015. In your textbook, this value is
rounded to 5.0. Using this as an estimate of σ, you can construct a Z-Interval, a
confidence interval for μ, the population mean. Press **STAT**, highlight **TESTS**
and select **7:Zinterval.**

```
EDIT CALC TESTS
1:Z-Test…
2:T-Test…
3:2-SampZTest…
4:2-SampTTest…
5:1-PropZTest…
6:2-PropZTest…
7↓ZInterval…
```

On the first line of the display, you can select **Data** or **Stats**. For this example,
select **Data** because you want to use the actual data which is in **L1**. Press
ENTER. Move to the next line and enter 5, your estimate of σ. On the next line,

enter **L1** for **LIST**. For **Freq**, enter **1**. For **C-Level** , enter **.99** for a 99%
confidence interval. Move the cursor to **Calculate.**

Press **ENTER** .

A 99% confidence interval estimate of μ , the population mean is (10.673,
14.179). The output display includes the sample mean (12.426), the sample
standard deviation (5.015), and the sample size (54).

◀

▸ Example 5 (pg. 275) Confidence Interval for μ (σ known)

In this example, $\bar{x} = 22.9$ years, n = 20, and a value for σ from previous studies is given as $\sigma = 1.5$ years. Construct a 90% confidence interval for μ, the mean age of all students currently enrolled at the college.

Press **STAT**, highlight **TESTS** and select **7:ZInterval**. In this example, you do not have the actual data. What you have are the summary statistics of the data, so select **Stats** and press **ENTER**. Enter the value for σ : **1.5**; enter the value for $\bar{x}$: **22.9**; enter the value for **n: 20**; and enter **.90** for **C-level**. Highlight **Calculate**.

Press **ENTER** .

Using a 90% confidence interval, you estimate that the average age of all students is between 22.348 and 23.452.

| ▶ Exercise 37 (pg. 279) | Newspaper Reading Times

Enter the data into **L1**. Press **STAT**, highlight **TESTS** and select **7:ZInterval**. Since you have entered the actual data points into **L1**, select **Data** for **Inpt** and press **ENTER**. Enter the value for σ , **1.5**. Set **LIST = L1, Freq = 1** and **C-level = .90**. Highlight **Calculate.**

```
ZInterval
 Inpt:DATA Stats
 σ:1.5
 List:L1
 Freq:1
 C-Level:.9
 Calculate
```

Now press **ENTER**.

```
ZInterval
 (8.4296,9.7037)
 x̄=9.066666667
 Sx=1.579632266
 n=15

■
```

Repeat the process and set **C-level = .99**.

```
ZInterval
 (8.0691,10.064)
 x̄=9.066666667
 Sx=1.579632266
 n=15

■
```

◀

▶ Exercise 51 (pg. 281) Using Technology

Enter the data into L1. In this example, no estimate of σ is given so you should use Sx, the sample standard deviation as a good approximation of σ siince n > 30. Press **STAT**, highlight **CALC**, select **1:1-Var Stats** and press **L1** **ENTER**. The sample standard deviation, Sx, is 11.19.

Press **STAT**, highlight **TESTS** and select **7:ZInterval**. For **Inpt**, select **Data**. For σ, enter **11.19**. Set **List** to **L1**, **Freq** to **1** and **C-level** to **.95**. Highlight **Calculate** and press **ENTER** .

```
ZInterval
 (303.5,311.25)
 x̄=307.375
 Sx=11.18971302
 n=32

■
```

Section 6.2

▶ **Example 3 (pg. 287)**   Constructing a Confidence Interval

In this example, n = 20, $\bar{x}$ = 6.93 and s = 0.42 and the underlying population is assumed to be normal. Find a 99% confidence interval for μ . First, notice that σ is unknown. The sample standard deviation, s, is not a good approximation of σ when n < 30. To construct the confidence interval for μ , the correct procedure under these circumstances (n < 30, σ is unknown and the population is assumed to be normally distributed) is to use a T-Interval.

Press **STAT**, highlight **TESTS**, scroll through the options and select **8:TInterval** and press **ENTER** . Select **Stats** for **Inpt** and press **ENTER**. Fill in $\bar{x}$, Sx, and n with the sample statistics. Set **C-level** to **.99**. Highlight **Calculate**.

Press **ENTER** .

▶ Exercise 21 (pg. 291) Deciding on a Distribution

In this example, n = 70, $\bar{x}$ = 1.25 and s = 0.01. Notice that σ is unknown. You can use s, the sample standard deviation, as a good approximation of σ in this case because n > 30. To calculate a 95 % confidence interval for μ , press **STAT**, highlight **TESTS** and select **7:ZInterval**. Fill in the screen with the appropriate information.

Calculate the confidence interval.

```
ZInterval
 (1.2477,1.2523)
 x̄=1.25
 n=70


■
```

▸ Exercise 23 (pg. 291) Deciding on a Distribution

Enter the data into **L1**. In this case, with n = 25 and σ unknown, and assuming that the population is normally distributed, you should use a Tinterval. Press **STAT**, highlight **TESTS** and select **8:TInterval**. Fill in the appropriate information.

Calculate the confidence interval.

Section 6.3

▶ Example 2 (pg. 295) Constructing a Confidence Interval for p

In this example, 1024 American adults are surveyed and 287 say that their
favorite sport is football (see Example 1, pg. 293). Construct a 95 % confidence
interval for p, the proportion of all Americans who say that their favorite sport is
football.

Press **STAT**, highlight **TESTS**, scroll through the options and select
A:1-PropZInt. The value for X is the number of American adults in the group of
1024 who said that football was their favorite sport, so **X = 287**. The number
who were surveyed is n, so **n = 1024**. Enter **.95** for **C-level**.

Highlight **Calculate** and press **ENTER** .

```
1-PropZInt
 (.25276,.30778)
 p=.2802734375
 n=1024
```

In the output display the confidence interval for p is (.25276, .30778). The sample
proportion, $\hat{p}$, is .28027 and the number surveyed is 1024.

◀

► Example 3 (pg. 296) Confidence Interval for p

From the graph, the sample proportion, $\hat{p}$, is 0.58 and n is 1001. Construct a
99% confidence interval for the proportion of adults who think that airplanes are
the safest mode of transportation. In order to construct this interval using the TI-
83, you must have a value for X, the number of people in the study who said that
airplanes were the safest mode of transportation. Multiply 0.58 by 1001 to get
this value. If this value is not a whole number, round to the nearest whole number.
For this example, X is 581.

Press **STAT**, highlight **TESTS** and select **A:1-PropZInt** by scrolling through the
options or by simply pressing **ALPHA** **A**. Enter the appropriate information
from the sample.

Highlight **Calculate** and press **ENTER**.

▶ Exercise 21 (pg. 299-300) Confidence Interval for p

a. To construct a 99% confidence interval for the proportion of men who favor irradiation of red meat, multiply .61 by 500 to obtain a value for X, the number of men in the survey who favor irradiation of red meat. Press **STAT**, highlight **TESTS** and select **A:1-PropZInt**. Fill in the appropriate values.

```
1-PropZInt
 x:305
 n:500
 C-Level:.99
 Calculate
```

Highlight **Calculate** and press **ENTER** .

```
1-PropZInt
 (.55381,.66619)
 p̂=.61
 n=500

■
```

b. To construct a 99 % confidence interval for the proportion of women who favor irradiation of red meat, multiply .44 by 500 to obtain a value for X, the number of women in the survey who favor irradiation of red meat. Press **STAT**, highlight **TESTS** and select **A:1-PropZInt**. Fill in the appropriate values. Highlight **Calculate** and press **ENTER** .

```
1-PropZInt
 (.38282,.49718)
 p̂=.44
 n=500

■
```

Notice that the two confidence intervals do not overlap. It is therefore unlikely that the proportion of males in the population who favor irradiation of red meat is the same as the proportion of females in the population who favor the irradiation of red meat.

◀

▶ Technology Lab (pg. 301) "Most Admired" Polls

1. Use the survey information to construct a 95% confidence interval for the proportion of people who would have chosen Pope John Paul II as their most admired man. Press **STAT**, highlight **TESTS** and select **A:1-PropInt**. Set X = 61 and n = 1011. Set **C-level** to **.95**, highlight **Calculate** and press **ENTER**

3. To construct a 95% confidence interval for the proportion of people who would have chosen Oprah Winfrey as their most admired female, you must calculate X, the number of people in the sample who chose Oprah. Multiply .04 by 1011 and round your answer to the nearest whole number. Press **STAT**, highlight **TESTS**, select **A:1-PropZInt** and fill in the appropriate information. Press **Calculate** and press **ENTER** .

4. To do one simulation, press **MATH**, highlight **PRB**, select **7:randBin(** and type in **1011** **,** **.07** **)** . The output is the number of successes in a survey of n = 1011 people. In this case, a "success" is choosing Oprah Winfrey as your most admired female. (Note: It takes approximately one minute for the TI-83 to do the calculation).

To run the simulation ten times use **7:randBin(1011,.07,10)**. (These simulations will take approximately 8 minutes). The output is a list of the number of successes in each of the 10 surveys. Calculate $\hat{p}$ for each of the surveys. $\hat{p}$ is equal to (number of successes)/1011. Use these 10 values of $\hat{p}$ to answer questions 4a and 4b

◀

Hypothesis Testing with One Sample

CHAPTER

7

Section 7.2

▸ **Example 4 (pg. 337)** Hypothesis Testing Using P-values

The hypothesis test, $H_o : \mu \geq 30$ vs. $H_a : \mu < 30$, is a left-tailed test. The sample statistics are $\bar{x} = 28.5$, s = 3.5 and n = 36. The sample size is greater than 30, so the **Z-Test** is the appropriate test. To run the test, press **STAT**, highlight **TESTS** and select **1:Z-Test**. Since you are using sample statistics for the analysis, select **Stats** for **Inpt** and press **ENTER**. For μ_0 enter 30, the value for μ in the null hypothesis. For σ enter **s**, the sample standard deviation. Enter **28.5** for $\bar{x}$ and **36** for **n**. On the next line, choose the appropriate alternative hypothesis and press **ENTER**. For this example, it is $< \mu_0$, a left-tailed test.

There are two choices for the output of this test. The first choice is **Calculate**. The output displays the alternative hypothesis, the calculated z-value, the P-value, $\bar{x}$ and n.

Since p = .005, which is less than α, the correct conclusion is to **Reject** H_o.

To view the second output option, press **STAT**, highlight **TESTS**, and select **1:Z-Test**. All the necessary information for this example is still stored in the calculator. Scroll down to the bottom line and select **DRAW**. A normal curve is displayed with the left-tail area of .0051 shaded. This shaded area is the area to the left of the calculated Z-value. The Z-value and the P-value are also displayed.

▶ **Example 5 (pg. 338)**   Hypothesis Testing Using P-values

This test is a two-tailed test for $H_o : \mu = 143260$ vs. $H_a : \mu \neq 143260$. The sample statistics are $\bar{x} = 135000$, s = 30000 and n = 30. Press STAT, highlight **TESTS** and select **1:Z-Test**. Choose **Stats** for **Inpt** and press ENTER. For μ_0 enter 143260, the value for μ in the null hypothesis. For σ, enter **s**, the sample standard deviation. Enter **135000** for $\bar{x}$ and **30** for **n**. On the next line, choose the appropriate alternative hypothesis and press ENTER. For this example, it is $\neq \mu_0$, a two-tailed test.

Highlight **Calculate** and press ENTER .

Or, highlight **Draw** and press ENTER.

Notice the P-value is equal to .1315. In this example, α is .05. Since the P-value is greater than α, the correct conclusion is to **Fail to Reject** H_o.

> **Exercise 31 (pg. 346)** Testing Claims Using P-values

Test the hypotheses: $H_o : \mu \le 260$ vs. $H_a : \mu > 260$.   The sample statistics are $\bar{x} = 265$, s = 55 and n = 85. Press **STAT**, highlight **TESTS** and select **1:Z-Test**. For **Inpt**, choose **Stats** and press **ENTER**. Fill the input screen with the appropriate information. Choose $> \mu_0$ for the alternative hypothesis and press **ENTER**. Highlight **Calculate** and press **ENTER**.

Or, highlight **Draw** and press **ENTER**.

The test statistic is $Z = 0.838$ and the P-value is .201. Since the P-value is greater than α, the correct conclusion is to **Fail to Reject** H_o.

▶ Exercise 35(pg. 347) Testing Claims Using P-values

Enter the data into **L1**. Notice that there is no one-tailed alternative hypothesis specified in this exercise. The test, therefore, is run as a two-tailed test and the hypotheses are: $H_o : \mu = 15$ vs. $H_a : \mu \neq 15$. You will need to find the sample standard deviation because the Z-test requires a value for σ. Press **STAT**, highlight **CALC** and choose **1:1-Var Stats** and press L1 **ENTER**. The sample statistics will be displayed on the screen. The value you need for the hypothesis test is Sx, the sample standard deviation, which is 4.29.

To perform the test, press **STAT**, highlight **TESTS** and select **1:Z-Test**. Since you have the actual data points for the analysis, select **Data** for **Inpt** and press **ENTER**. Fill in the input screen with the appropriate information and select $\neq \mu_0$, as the alternative hypothesis and press **ENTER**. Highlight **Calculate** and press **ENTER**

Or, highlight **Draw** and press **ENTER**.

Since the P-value is greater than α, the correct conclusion is to **Fail to Reject** H_o.

▶ Exercise 41 (pg. 348) Testing Claims

This is a hypothesis test for $H_o : \mu \leq 28$ vs. $H_a : \mu > 28$. Since n > 30, the appropriate test is the Z-Test. This procedure requires a value for σ. In cases with n > 30, the sample standard deviation, s, can be used to approximate σ. Begin the analysis by entering the 36 data points into **L1**. Press **STAT**, highlight **CALC** and choose **1:1-Var Stats** and press **L1 ENTER**. The sample statistics will be displayed on the screen. The value you need for the hypothesis test is Sx, the sample standard deviation, which is 22.13.

To run the hypothesis test, press **STAT**, highlight **TESTS** and select **1:Z-Test**. Since you have the actual data points for the analysis, select **Data** for **Inpt** and press **ENTER**. Enter **28** for μ_0 and enter **22.13** for σ. The data is stored in **L1** and **Freq** is **1**. The alternate hypothesis is a right-tailed test so select $> \mu_0$ and press **ENTER**.

```
Z-Test
 Inpt:DATA Stats
 μ0:28
 σ:22.13
 List:L₁
 Freq:1
 μ:≠μ0 <μ0 >μ0
 Calculate Draw
```

To run the test, select **Calculate** and press **ENTER**.

```
Z-Test
 μ>28
 z=1.317969574
 P=.0937569803
 x̄=32.86111111
 Sx=22.12839517
 n=36
```

Or, select **Draw** and press **ENTER**.

Since the P-value of .0938 is greater than α, the correct conclusion is to **Fail to Reject** H_o.

Section 7.3

▶ **Example 6 (pg. 355)**   Using P-values with a T-Test

This test is a two-tailed test of $H_o : \mu = 132$ vs. $H_a : \mu \neq 132$. The sample statistics are $\bar{x} = 141$, $s = 20$ and $n = 11$. Since n < 30, the test is a T-Test if you assume that the underlying population is approximately normally distributed. Press **STAT**, highlight **TESTS** and select **2:T-Test**. Choose **Stats** for **Inpt** and press **ENTER**. Fill in the following information: $\mu_0 = \mathbf{132}$, $\bar{x} = \mathbf{141}$, **Sx = 20** and **n = 11**. Choose the two-tailed alternative hypothesis, $\neq \mu_0$, and press **ENTER**. Highlight **Calculate** and press **ENTER**

```
T-Test
 μ≠132
 t=1.492481156
 P=.1664335286
 x̄=141
 Sx=20
 n=11
```

Or, highlight **Draw** and press **ENTER**.

```
t=1.4925    P=.1664
```

Since the P-value is greater than α, the correct conclusion is to **Fail to Reject** H_o.

◀

▶ Exercise 29 (pg. 358) Testing Claims Using P-values

The correct hypothesis test is $H_o : \mu = 3$ vs. $H_a : \mu < 3$. Enter the data into L1. Since n < 30, the appropriate test is the T-Test, if you assume that the underlying population is approximately normal. Press STAT, highlight **TESTS** and select **2:T-Test**. Select **Data** for **Inpt** and press ENTER. Fill in the screen with the necessary information, choose **Calculate** and press ENTER.

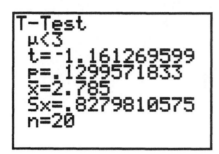

Or, choose **Draw** and press ENTER.

Since the P-value is greater than α, the correct conclusion is to **Fail to Reject** H_o.

▶ Exercise 37(pg. 359) Deciding on a Distribution

This test is a left-tailed test of $H_o: \mu \geq 21$ vs. $H_a: \mu < 21$. The sample statistics are $\bar{x} = 19$, $s = 4$ and $n = 5$. Since $n < 30$ and gas mileage is normally distributed, the appropriate test is the **T-Test**. Press **STAT**, highlight **TESTS** and select **2:T-Test**. Fill in the screen with the necessary information and choose **Calculate** and press **ENTER**.

Or, choose **Draw** and press **ENTER**.

Since the P-value is greater than α, the correct conclusion is to **Fail to Reject** H_o.

▸ Exercise 39 (pg. 359) Deciding on a Distribution

This test is a left-tailed test of $H_o: \mu \geq 21$ vs. $H_a: \mu < 21$. The sample statistics are $\bar{x} = 19$ and n = 5. Since the population standard deviation is known, $\sigma = 5$, the appropriate test is the **Z-Test**. Press **STAT**, highlight **TESTS** and select **1:Z-Test**. Fill in the screen with the necessary information and choose **Calculate** and press **ENTER**.

Or, choose **Draw** and press **ENTER**.

Since the P-value is greater than α, the correct conclusion is to **Fail to Reject** H_o.

Compare these results to the t-test results in Exercise 37. In both cases, you fail to reject the null hypothesis since the P-value is greater than α.

◀

Section 7.4

> ▶ **Example 1 (pg. 361)** Hypothesis Test for a Proportion

This hypothesis test is a left-tailed test of: $H_o: p \geq .20$ vs. $H_a: p < .20$. The sample statistics are $\hat{p} = .15$ and n = 100. Press **STAT**, highlight **TESTS** and select **5:1-PropZTest**. This test requires a value for p_0, which is the value for p in the null hypothesis. Enter **.20** for p_0. Next, a value for X is required. X is the number of "successes" in the sample. In this example, a success is " having an allergy". Since 15% of the individuals in the sample say that they have an allergy, **X** is equal to .15 times 100 or **15**. Next, enter the value for n. Select $< p_0$ for the alternative hypothesis and press **ENTER**.

Highlight **Calculate** and press **ENTER**.

Or, highlight **Draw** and press **ENTER**.

Since the P-value is greater than α, the correct conclusion is to **Fail to Reject** H_o.

◄

▶ **Example 3 (pg. 363)** Hypothesis Test for a Proportion

The hypothesis test is: $H_o: p \leq .55$ vs. $H_a: p > .55$. The sample statistics are $n = 425$ and $X = 255$. Press **STAT**, highlight **TESTS** and select **5:1-PropZTest**. Enter the necessary information. Highlight **Calculate** and press **ENTER**.

```
1-PropZTest
 Prop>.55
 z=2.071938535
 P=.0191355209
 P=.6
 n=425
■
```

Or, highlight **Draw** and press **ENTER**.

Since the P-value is less than α, the correct conclusion is to **Reject** H_o.

◄

▶ Exercise 11 (pg. 364) Testing Claims

Use a right-tailed hypothesis test to test the hypotheses: $H_o : p \leq .30$ vs. $H_a : p > .30$. The sample statistics are n = 1050 and $\hat{p} = .32$. Multiply n times $\hat{p}$ to find X, the number of consumers in the sample who have stopped purchasing a product because it pollutes the environment. Press **STAT**, highlight **TESTS** and select **5:1-PropZTest**. Enter the necessary information. Highlight **Calculate** and press **ENTER**.

Or, highlight **Draw** and press **ENTER**.

Since the P-value is .greater than α, the correct conclusion is to **Fail to Reject** H_o.

▸ Exercise 13 (pg. 365) Testing Claims

Use a two-tailed hypothesis test to test: $H_o : p = .60$ vs. $H_a : p \neq .60$. The sample statistics are n = 1762 and X = 1004. Press **STAT**, highlight **TESTS** and select **5:1-PropZTest**. Enter the necessary information. Highlight **Calculate** and press **ENTER**.

Or, highlight **Draw** and press **ENTER**.

Since the P-value is .0097 and is less than α, the correct conclusion is to **Reject** H_o.

◂

▸ Technology Lab (pg. 366) The Case of the Vanishing Women

Exercise 1: Use the TI-83 to run the hypothesis test and compare your results to the MINITAB results shown in the display at the bottom of pg. 366. Use a two-tailed test to test the hypotheses: $H_o : p = 0.53$ vs. $H_a : p \neq 0.53$. The sample statistics are X = 102 women and n = 350 people selected from the Boston City Directory. Press **STAT**, highlight **TESTS** and select **5:1-PropZTest**. Fill in the appropriate information highlight **Calculate** and press **ENTER** or, highlight **Draw** and press **ENTER**.

Exercise 4: In the first stage of the jury selection process, 350 people are selected and 102 of them are women. So, at this stage, the proportion of women is 102 out of 350, or 0.2914. From this population of 350 people, a sample of 100 people is selected at random and only nine are women. Test the claim that the proportion of women in the population is 0.2914. Use a two-tailed test to test the hypotheses: $H_o : p = 0.2914$ vs. $H_a : p \neq 0.2914$. The sample statistics are X = 9 women and n = 100 people. Press **STAT**, highlight **TESTS** and select **5:1-PropZTest**. Fill in the appropriate information, Highlight **Calculate** and press **ENTER** or highlight **Draw** and press **ENTER**.

◀

Hypothesis Testing with Two Samples

CHAPTER

8

Section 8.1

▶ Example 2 (pg. 394) Two-Sample Z-Test

Test the claim that the average daily cost for meals and lodging when vacationing in Texas is less than the average costs when vacationing in Washington State. Designate Texas as population 1 and Washington as population 2. The appropriate hypothesis test is a left-tailed test of $H_o: \mu_1 \geq \mu_2$ vs $H_a: \mu_1 < \mu_2$. The sample statistics are displayed in the table at the top of pg. 394. Each sample size is greater than 30, so the correct test is a Two-sample Z-Test.

Press STAT, highlight **TESTS** and select **3:2-SampZTest**. Since you are using the sample statistics for your analysis, select **Stats** for **Inpt** and press ENTER. The first item to enter is a value for σ_1. The sample standard deviation, s_1, can be used as an approximation of σ_1. Enter 15 for σ_1. Enter 28 for σ_2. Next, enter the mean and sample size for group 1: $\bar{x}_1 = 208$ and $n_1 = 50$. Continue by entering the mean and sample size for group 2: $\bar{x}_2 = 218$ and $n_2 = 35$.

Use the down arrow to display the next line. This line displays the three possible alternative hypotheses for testing: $\mu_1 \neq \mu_2$, $\mu_1 > \mu_2$, or $\mu_1 < \mu_2$. For this example, select $< \mu_2$ and press ENTER. Scroll down to the next line and select **Calculate** or **Draw**.

The output for **Calculate** is displayed on two pages. (Notice that the only piece of information on the second page is n_2.)

```
2-SampZTest
 µ1<µ2
 z=-1.928074718
 P=.0269228477
 x̄1=208
 x̄2=218
↓n1=50
```

The output for **Draw** contains a graph of the normal curve with the area associated with the test statistic shaded.

```
z=-1.9281    P=.0269
```

Both outputs display the P-value, which is .0269. Since the P-value is greater than α, the correct decision is to **Fail to Reject** H_o. At the 1% level of significance, there is not enough evidence to support the claim that the average cost for meals and lodging when vacationing in Texas is less than the average cost when vacationing in Washington state.

◀

▸ Exercise 9 (pg. 396) Testing the Difference between Two Means

The appropriate hypothesis test is a two-tailed test of $H_o: \mu_1 = \mu_2$ vs $H_a: \mu_1 \neq \mu_2$. Designate Tire Type A as population 1 and Tire Type B as population 2. Press **STAT**, highlight **TESTS** and select **3:2-SampZTest**. For **Inpt,** select **Stats** and press **ENTER**. Enter the sample standard deviations as approximations of σ_1 and σ_2. Next, enter the sample statistics for each group.

Select $\neq \mu_2$ as the alternative hypothesis and press **ENTER**. Scroll down to the next line and select **Calculate** or **Draw** and press **ENTER**.

The output for **Calculate** is:

The output for **Draw** is:

The test statistic, z, is −2.786 and the p-value is .0053. Since the P-value is less than α, the correct decision is to **Reject** H_o. ◀

▶ Exercise 19 (pg. 397) Testing the Difference between 2 Means

Enter the data from 1981 into **L1** and enter the data from the more recent study
into **L2**. The hypothesis test is: $H_o: \mu_1 \le \mu_2$ vs $H_a: \mu_1 > \mu_2$. Since both n_1
and n_2 equal 30, the Two-Sample Z-Test can be used. In order to use this test,
values for σ_1 and σ_2 are required. The sample standard deviations, s_1 and s_2
can be used as approximations for σ_1 and σ_2 when both n_1 and n_2 are greater
than or equal to 30. To find the standard deviations, press **STAT**, highlight
CALC and select **1:1-Var Stats** and press **L1** **ENTER**. The value for Sx is the
sample standard deviation for the 1981 data. Next, press **STAT**, highlight
CALC and select **1:1-Var Stats**, press **L2** **ENTER**. The value for Sx is the
sample standard deviation for the more recent data.

To run the hypothesis, press **STAT**, highlight **TESTS** and select **3:2-
SampZTest**. For **Inpt** select **Data** and press **ENTER**. Enter the sample
standard deviations as approximations of σ_1 and σ_2. For **List1**, press **2nd [L1]**
and for **List2** press **2nd [L2]** .

```
2-SampZTest
 Inpt:Data Stats
 σ1:.49
 σ2:.33
 List1:L1
 List2:L2
 Freq1:0
↓Freq2:1
```

Select $> \mu_2$ as the alternative hypothesis and press **ENTER**. Scroll down to the
next line and select **Calculate** or **Draw** and press **ENTER**.

The output for **Calculate** is:

```
2-SampZTest
 μ1>μ2
 z=4.975681069
 p=3.2559526E-7
 x̄1=2.13
 x̄2=1.593333333
↓Sx1=.490003519
```

The output for **Draw** is:

Since the P-value is smaller than α, the correct decision is to **Reject** H_o.

> **Exercise 29 (pg. 400)** Confidence Intervals for $\mu_1 - \mu_2$

Construct a confidence interval for $\mu_1 - \mu_2$, the difference between two population means. Designate the group using the herbal supplement as population 1 and the group using the placebo as population 2. The sample statistics for group 1 are: $\bar{x}_1 = 3.2$, $s_1 = 3.3$ and $n_1 = 42$. The sample statistics for group 2 are: $\bar{x}_2 = 4.1$, $s_2 = 3.9$ and $n_2 = 42$.

Press **STAT**, highlight **TESTS** and select **9:2-SampZInt**. Since you are using the sample statistics for your analysis, select **Stats** for **Inpt** and press **ENTER**. Enter the sample standard deviations as approximations for σ_1 and σ_2. Enter the sample means and sample sizes for each group.

```
2-SampZInt
 Inpt:Data Stats
 σ1:3.3
 σ2:3.9
 x̄1:3.2
 n1:42
 x̄2:4.1
↓n2:42
```

Scroll down to the next line and type in the confidence level of .95. Scroll down to the next line and press **ENTER**.

```
2-SampZInt
 (-2.445,.64505)
 x̄1=3.2
 x̄2=4.1
 n1=42
 n2=42
■
```

A 95 % confidence interval for the difference in the population means is (-2.445, .64505). Since this interval contains 0, the correct conclusion is that there is no difference in the means of the two groups. The herbal supplement does *not* appear to help in weight loss.

Section 8.2

▶ Example 1 (pg. 404) Two Sample t-Test

To test whether the mean stopping distances are different, use a two-tailed test: $H_o: \mu_1 = \mu_2$ vs $H_a: \mu_1 \neq \mu_2$. The sample statistics are found in the table at the top of pg. 404 in your textbook.

Press **STAT**, highlight **TESTS**, and select **4:2-SampTTest**. Since you are inputting the sample statistics, select **Stats** and press **ENTER**. Enter the sample information from the two samples. Select $\neq \mu_2$ as the alternative hypothesis and press **ENTER**. Scroll down to the next line. On this line, select **NO** because the variances are NOT assumed to be equal and therefore, you do not want a pooled estimate of the standard deviation. Press **ENTER**. Scroll down to the next line, highlight **Calculate** and press **ENTER**.

```
2-SampTTest
 µ1≠µ2
 t=-1.495915184
 P=.162535817
 df=11.10815972
 x̄1=51
↓x̄2=55
```

The output (shown above) for **Calculate** displays the alternative hypothesis, the test statistic, the P-value, the degrees of freedom and the sample statistics. Notice the degrees of freedom = 11.108. In cases, such as this one, in which the population variances are not assumed to be equal, the calculator calculates an adjusted degrees of freedom, rather than using the smaller of (n_1 -1) and (n_2 -1).

If you choose **Draw**, the output includes a graph with the area associated with the P-value shaded.

t=-1.4959 P=.1625

▶ Example 2 (pg. 405) Two Sample t-Test

To test the claim that the mean range of the manufacturer's cordless phone is greater than the mean range of the competitor's phone, use a right-tailed test with $H_o: \mu_1 \le \mu_2$ vs $H_a: \mu_1 > \mu_2$. Designate the manufacturer's data as population 1 and the competitor's data as population 2. Use the Two-Sample T-Test for the analysis, and use the pooled variance option because the population variances are assumed to be equal in this example. The sample statistics are found in the table at the top of pg. 405 in your textbook.

Press **STAT**, highlight **TESTS**, and select **4:2-SampTTest**
. Fill in the input screen with the sample statistics. Select $> \mu_2$ for the alternative hypothesis and press **ENTER**. Select **YES** for **Pooled** and press **ENTER**. To do the analysis, select **Calculate** and press **ENTER**.

```
2-SampTTest
 µ1>µ2
 t=1.811358919
 p=.0404131295
 df=28
 x̄1=1275
↓x̄2=1250
■
```

```
2-SampTTest
 µ1>µ2
↑Sx1=45
 Sx2=30
 SxP=37.7136769
 n1=14
 n2=16
■
```

The two-page output display (shown above) includes the alternative hypothesis, the test statistic, the P-value, degrees of freedom, the sample statistics and the pooled standard deviation (Sxp = 37.7)

If you select **Draw**, the display includes a graph with the shaded area associated with the test statistic, the P-value and the test statistic.

Since the P-value is less than α, the correct decision is to **Reject** H_o

◀

> ▸ Exercise 15 (pg. 407) Testing the Difference between 2 Means

Designate the small cars as population 1 and the midsize cars as population 2.
Test the hypothesis: H_o: $\mu_1 = \mu_2$ vs. H_a: $\mu_1 \neq \mu_2$. The sample statistics are:
$\bar{x}_1 = 23.1$, $s_1 = 8.69$, $n_1 = 14$, $\bar{x}_2 = 25.3$, $s_2 = 7.21$ and $n_2 = 23$. Use the Two-
Sample T-test with the pooled variance option. Press **STAT**, highlight **TESTS**
and select **4:2-SampTTest**. Choose **Stats** for **Inpt** and press **ENTER**. Enter the
sample statistics. Select $\neq \mu_2$ as the alternative hypothesis and press **ENTER**.
Select **YES** for **Pooled** and press **ENTER**. Highlight **Calculate** and press
ENTER.

```
2-SampTTest
 μ1≠μ2
 t=-.8328515082
 P=.4105758669
 df=35
 x̄1=23.1
↓x̄2=25.3
■
```

Notice that the test statistic = -0.833, and the P-value is .411. Since the P-value
is greater than α, the correct decision is to **Fail to Reject** H_o.

◀

▶ Exercise 23(pg. 409) Testing the difference between 2 Means

Designate the "Old curriculum" as population 1 and the "New curriculum" as population 2 and test the hypothesis: $H_o : \mu_1 \geq \mu_2$ vs. $H_a : \mu_1 < \mu_2$. Press STAT, select **1:Edit** and enter the data sets into **L1** (Old curriculum) and **L2** (New curriculum). Press STAT, highlight **TESTS** and select **4:2-SampTTest**. For this analysis, you are using the actual data so select **Data** for **Inpt** and press ENTER. Fill in the input screen with the appropriate information. Choose $< \mu_2$ as the alternative hypothesis and press ENTER. Choose **YES** for **Pooled** and press ENTER. Highlight **Calculate** and press ENTER.

```
2-SampTTest
 µ1<µ2
 t=-4.29519297
 p=5.0503069ε-5
 df=42
 x̄1=56.68421053
↓x̄2=67.4
```

Since the P-value (.00005) is less than α, the correct decision is to **Reject** H_o. This means that the data supports H_a, indicating that the new method of teaching reading produces higher reading test scores than the old method. The recommendation is to change to the new method.

◀

> ▶ Exercise 25 (pg. 410) Confidence Intervals

Compare the mean calorie content of grilled chicken sandwiches from Arby's restaurants to similar chicken sandwiches from McDonald's using a confidence interval. For this exercise, assume that the populations are normal and the variances are equal. Also, notice that the sample sizes are both less than 30. The appropriate confidence interval technique is the Two-Sample t-interval.

Press **STAT**, highlight **TESTS** and select **0:2-SampTInt**. For **Inpt**, select **Stats** and press **ENTER**. Enter the sample statistics from the two sets of data. Designate Arby's as population 1 and McDonald's as population 2. Choose **.95** for **C-level** and choose **YES** for **Pooled** and press **ENTER**. Scroll down to the next line and press **ENTER** to **Calculate** the confidence interval.

```
2-SampTInt
 (-15.66, -4.337)
 df=25
 x̄1=230
 x̄2=240
 Sx1=6.2
↓Sx2=8.1
```

The output displays the 95 % confidence interval for (μ_1 - μ_2) and the sample statistics. One way to interpret the confidence interval is to state that "the difference in mean calorie content of grilled chicken sandwiches at the two restaurants is between -15.66 and -4.337." This means that the mean calorie content of the Arby's sandwiches is anywhere from 4.337 to 15.66 less than that of McDonald's.

◀

▶ **Exercise 27 (pg. 410)** Confidence Intervals

Compare the mean cholesterol content of grilled sandwiches from Arby's to similar sandwiches from McDonald's using a confidence interval. For this exercise, assume the populations are normal but do NOT assume equal variances.

Press **STAT**, highlight **TESTS** and select **0:2-SampTInt**. For **Inpt**, select **Stats** and press **ENTER**. Enter the sample statistics from the table displayed in Exercise 27. Designate Arby's as population 1 and McDonald's as population 2. Choose **.90** for **C-level** and choose **NO** for **Pooled** and press **ENTER**. Scroll down to the next line and press **ENTER** to **Calculate** the confidence interval.

```
2-SampTInt
 (-.9816,2.9816)
 df=24.37225626
 x̄1=61
 x̄2=60
 Sx1=3.59
↓Sx2=2.41
```

The output displays the 90 % confidence interval for (μ_1 - μ_2), the adjusted degrees of freedom and the sample statistics. The confidence interval states that the mean cholesterol content for Arby's sandwiches is anywhere from 0.98 less than to 2.98 more than that of McDonald's. Since this interval contains 0, you cannot conclude that there is any difference in mean cholesterol content.

◀

Section 8.3

▶ Example 2 (pg. 414)   The Paired t-Test

In this example, the data is paired data, with two scores for each of the 8 golfers. Enter the scores that each golfer gave as his or her most recent score into L1. Enter the scores achieved after using the newly designated clubs into L2. Next, you must create a set of differences, d = (old score) - (new score). To create this set, move the cursor to highlight the label **L3,** found at the top of the third column, and press ██████. Notice that the cursor is flashing on the bottom line of the display. Press **2ⁿᵈ [L1] - 2ⁿᵈ [L2]**

L1	L2	▓ 3
89	83	------
84	83	
96	92	
82	84	
74	76	
92	91	
85	80	
L3 =L₁−L₂		

and press ██████.

L1	L2	L3 3
89	83	6
84	83	1
96	92	4
82	84	-2
74	76	-2
92	91	1
85	80	5
L3(1)=6		

Each value in **L3** is the difference L1 - L2.

To test the claim that golfers can lower their scores using the manufacturer's newly designed clubs, the hypothesis test is: $H_o : \mu_d \leq 0$ vs. $H_a : \mu_d > 0$. Press ██████, highlight **TESTS** and select **2:T-Test**. In this example, you are using the actual data to do the analysis, so select **Data** for **Inpt** and press ██████. The value for μ_o is **0**, the value in the null hypothesis. The set of differences is found in **L3**, so set **List** to **L3**. Set **Freq** equal to **1**. Choose $> \mu_o$ as the alternative hypothesis and highlight **Calculate** and press ██████.

```
T-Test
 μ>0
 t=1.498259585
 P=.0888692418
 x̄=1.625
 Sx=3.067688753
 n=8
```

You can also highlight **DRAW** and press ENTER.

Since the P-value is less than α, the correct decision is to **Reject** H_o.

◀

▶ Exercise 17(pg. 418) Paired Difference Test

Press **STAT** and select **1:Edit.** Enter the students' scores on the first SAT into **L1** and their scores on the second Sat into **L2**. Since this is paired data, create a column of differences, d = (first SAT) - (second SAT). To create the differences, move the cursor to highlight the label **L3,** found at the top of the third column, and press **ENTER**. Notice that the cursor is flashing on the bottom line of the display. Press **2ⁿᵈ [L1]** - **2ⁿᵈ [L2]** and press **ENTER**.

L1	L2	L3	3
445	446	-1	
510	571	-61	
429	517	-88	
452	478	-26	
629	610	19	
433	453	-20	
551	516	35	

L3(1)= -1

Each value in **L3** is the difference **L1 - L2**.

To test the claim that students' verbal SAT scores improved the second time they took the verbal SAT, the hypotheses are:: $H_o: \mu_d \geq 0$ vs. $H_a: \mu_d < 0$. Press **STAT**, highlight **TESTS** and select **2:T-Test**. In this example, you are using the actual data to do the analysis, so select **Data** for **Inpt** and press **ENTER**. The value for μ_o is **0**, the value in the null hypothesis. The set of differences is found in **L3**, so set **List** to **L3**. Set **Freq** equal to **1**. Choose < μ_o as the alternative hypothesis and highlight **Calculate** and press **ENTER**.

```
T-Test
 μ<0
 t=-3.001096523
 p=.0051086649
 x̄=-33.71428571
 Sx=42.03373841
 n=14
```

Or, highlight **DRAW** and press **ENTER**.

Since the P-value is less than α, the correct decision is to **Reject** H_o.

> ▶ Exercise 25(pg. 421)   Confidence Interval for μ_d

Press **STAT** and select **1:Edit**. Enter the data for "hours of sleep without the drug" into **L1** and the data for "hours of sleep using the new drug" into **L2**. Since this is paired data, create a column of differences, **d = L1 - L2**. To create the differences, move the cursor to highlight the label **L3**, found at the top of the third column, and press **ENTER**. Notice that the cursor is flashing on the bottom line of the display. Press 2nd **[L1]** - 2nd **[L2]** and press **ENTER**. Each value in **L3** is the difference **L1 - L2**.

To construct a confidence interval for μ_d, press **STAT**, highlight **TESTS** and select **8:Tinterval**. For **Inpt**, select **Data**, for **List**, enter **L3**. Make sure that **Freq** is equal to **1**, and the **C-level** is **90**. Highlight **Calculate** and press **ENTER**.

```
TInterval
 (-1.763,-1.287)
 x̄=-1.525
 Sx=.5422176685
 n=16

■
```

The confidence interval for μ_d is -1.763 to -1.287. This means that the average difference in hours of sleep is 1.287 hours to 1.763 hours more for patients using the new drug.

◀

Section 8.4

▶ Example 1 (pg. 424) Testing the Difference Between p_1 and p_2

To test the claim that there is a difference in the proportion of female Internet users who plan to shop On-line and the proportion of male Internet users who plan to shop On-line, the correct hypothesis test is: $H_o: p_1 = p_2$ vs $H_a: p_1 \neq p_2$. Designate the females as population 1 and the males as population 2. The sample statistics are $n_1 = 200$, $p_1 = .30$, $n_2 = 250$, and $p_2 = .38$. To conduct this test using the TI-83, you need values for x_1, the number of females in the sample who plan to shop On-line, and x_2, he number of males who plan to shop On-line. To calculate x_1, multiply n_1 times p_1. To calculate x_2, multiply n_2 times p_2.

Press **STAT**, highlight **TESTS** and select **6:2-PropZTest** and fill in the appropriate information. Highlight **Calculate** and press **ENTER**.

```
2-PropZTest
 P1≠P2
 z=-1.774615984
 P=.0759612188
 p̂1=.3
 p̂2=.38
↓p̂=.3444444444
```

The output displays the alternative hypothesis, the test statistic, the P-value, the sample statistics and the weighted estimate of the population proportion, $\hat{p}$.
Since the P-value is less than α, the correct decision is to **Reject** H_o.

> **Exercise 9 (pg. 426)** The Difference Between Two Proportions

Designate the 1991 data as population 1 and the more recent data as population 2 and test the hypotheses: $H_o: p_1 = p_2$ vs $H_a: p_1 \neq p_2$. The sample statistics are $n_1 = 1539$, $x_1 = 520$, $n_2 = 2055$, and $x_2 = 865$.

Press **STAT**, highlight **TESTS** and select **6:2-PropZTest** and fill in the appropriate information. Highlight **Calculate** and press **ENTER**.

```
2-PropZTest
 P1≠P2
 z=-5.06166817
 P=4.1630154E-7
 p̂1=.3378817414
 p̂2=.4209245742
↓p̂=.3853644964
■
```

Since the P-value (.0000004163) is less than α, the correct decision is to **Reject** H_o. This indicates that the proportion of adults using alternative medicines has changed since 1991.

◀

▶ Exercise 19 (pg. 428)   Confidence Interval for $p_1 - p_2$.

Construct a confidence interval to compare the proportion of students who had planned to study engineering several years ago to the proportion currently planning on studying engineering. Designate the earlier survey results as population 1 and the recent survey results as population 2. The sample statistics are $n_1 = 977000$, $p_1 = 11.7\%$, $n_2 = 1085000$, and $p_2 = 8.5\%$. To calculate x_1 multiply n_1 times p_1. To calculate x_2, multiply n_2 times p_2. (Use .117 for p_1 and .085 for p_2.)

Press **STAT**, highlight **TESTS** and select **B:2-PropZInt** and fill in the appropriate information. Highlight **Calculate** and press **ENTER**.

```
2-PropZInt
 (.03117,.03283)
 p̂1=.117
 p̂2=.085
 n1=977000
 n2=1085000
```

The confidence interval (.03117, .03283) indicates that the proportion of students having chosen engineering in the past is between 3.12 % and 3.28 % higher than the proportion of students currently choosing engineering. Notice how narrow the confidence interval is. This is due to the very large sample sizes.

◀

> ▶ Technology Lab (pg. 429) Tails Over Heads

Exercise 1 - 2: Test the hypotheses: H_o : P(Heads) = .5 vs. H_a : P(Heads) $\neq$ .5 using the one sample test of a proportion. Press **STAT**, highlight **TESTS** and select **5:1-PropZTest.** For this example, p_o = .5. Using Casey's data, X = 5772 and n = 11902. The alternative hypothesis is $\neq$. Highlight **Calculate** and press **ENTER**.

```
1-PropZTest
 prop≠.5
 z=-3.281504874
 P=.0010326665
 p̂=.4849605108
 n=11902
```

Since the P-value is less than α , the correct decision is to **Reject** H_o .

Exercise 3: The histogram at the top of the page is a graph of 500 simulations of Casey's experiment. Each simulation represents 11902 flips of a fair coin. The bars of the histogram represent frequencies. Use the histogram to determine how often 5772 or fewer heads occurred.

To simulate this experiment, you must use an alternative technology. The TI-83 does not have the memory capacity to do this experiment.

Exercise 4: To compare the mint dates of the coins, run the hypothesis test: H_o : μ_1 = μ_2 vs. H_a : μ_1 $\neq$ μ_2 . Designate the Philadelphia data as population 1 and the Denver data as population 2.

Press **STAT**, highlight **TESTS** and select **3:2-SampZTest**. Choose **Stats** for **Inpt** and press **ENTER**. Enter the sample statistics. Use the sample standard deviations as approximations to the population standard deviations. Select $\neq$ μ_2 as the alternative hypothesis and press **ENTER**. Highlight **Calculate** and press **ENTER**.

```
2-SampZTest
 µ1≠µ2
 z=8.801919011
 P=1.363493E-18
 x̄1=1984.8
 x̄2=1983.4
↓n1=7133
```

Since the P-value is extremely small, the correct decision is to **Reject** H_o.

Exercise 5: To compare the average mint value of coins minted in Philadelphia to those minted in Denver, run the hypothesis test: $H_o: \mu_1 = \mu_2$ vs. $H_a: \mu_1 \neq \mu_2$. Designate the Philadelphia data as population 1 and the Denver data as population 2.

Press **STAT**, highlight **TESTS** and select **3:2-SampZTest**. Choose **Stats** for **Inpt** and press **ENTER**. Enter the sample statistics. Use the sample standard deviations as approximations to the population standard deviations. Select $\neq \mu_2$ as the alternative hypothesis and press **ENTER**. Highlight **Calculate** and press **ENTER**. Since the P-value is extremely small, the correct decision is to **Reject** H_o.

◀

Correlation and Regression

CHAPTER

9

Section 9.1

▶ Example 3 (pg. 444) Constructing a Scatter plot

Press **STAT**, highlight **1:Edit** and clear **L1** and **L2**. Enter the X-values into **L1** and the Y-values into **L2**. Press **2ⁿᵈ [STAT PLOT]**, select **1:Plot1**, turn **ON** Plot 1 and press **ENTER**. For **Type** of graph, select the **scatter plot** which is the first selection. Press **ENTER**. Enter **L1** for **Xlist** and **L2** for **Ylist**. Highlight the first selection, the small square, for the type of **Mark**. Press **ENTER**. Press **ZOOM** and 9 to select **ZoomStat**.

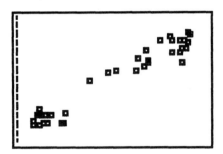

This graph shows a positive linear correlation.

◀

▶ **Example 5 (pg. 447)**   Finding a Correlation Coefficient

For this example, use the data from Example 3 on pg. 444. Enter the X-values
into **L1** and the Y-values into **L2**. In order to calculate r, the correlation
coefficient, you must turn **On** the **Diagnostic** command. Press **2nd [CATALOG]**
(Note: CATALOG is found above the ▓ key). The CATALOG of functions will
appear on the screen. Use the down arrow to scroll to the **DiagnosticOn**
command.

```
CATALOG          ▓
 Degree
 DelVar
 DependAsk
 DependAuto
 det(
 DiagnosticOff
▶DiagnosticOn
```

Press **ENTER** **ENTER**.

Press **STAT**, highlight **CALC**, select **4:LinReg(ax+b)** and press **ENTER**
ENTER. (Note: This command requires that you specify which lists contain the
X-values and Y-values. If you do not specify these lists, the defaults are used.
The defaults are: **L1** for the X-values and **L2** for the Y-values.)

```
LinReg
 y=ax+b
 a=11.8244078
 b=35.30117105
 r²=.9404868083
 r=.9697869912
```

The correlation coefficient is r = .9697869912. This suggests a strong positive
linear correlation between X and Y.

◀

▶ Exercise 13 (pg. 455) Constructing a Scatter plot and
                              Determining r

Enter the X-values into **L1** and the Y-values into **L2**. Press **2nd [STAT PLOT]** ,
select **1:Plot1**, turn **ON** Plot 1 and press ENTER. For **Type** of graph, select the
scatter plot. Enter **L1** for **Xlist** and **L2** for **Ylist**. Press ZOOM and 9 to select
ZoomStat.

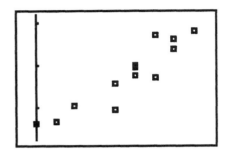

To calculate r, press STAT, highlight **CALC** and select **4:LinReg(ax+b)** and
press ENTER ENTER.

The scatter plot shows a strong positive linear correlation. This is confirmed by
the r-value of 0.923.

◀

▶ Example 21 (pg. 456)   Testing Claims

To test the significance of the population correlation coefficient, ρ, the appropriate hypothesis test is: $\rho = 0$ vs. $\rho \neq 0$. To run the test, enter the X-values into **L1** and the Y-values into **L2**. Press **STAT**, highlight **TESTS** and select **E:LinRegTTest**. Enter **L1** for **Xlist**, **L2** for **Ylist**, and 1 for **Freq**. On the next line, β and ρ, select $\neq 0$ and press **ENTER**. Leave the next line, RegEQ, blank. Highlight **Calculate.**

Press **ENTER**.

```
LinRegTTest
 y=a+bx
 β≠0 and ρ≠0
 t=7.935104115
 P=7.0576131E-6
 df=11
↓a=34.6169265
```

The output displays several pieces of information describing the relationship between X and Y. What you are interested in for this example are the following: the test statistic (t = 7.935), the P-value (p = 7.0576131E-6) and the r value (r = .922649886). Since the P-value is less than α, the correct decision is to **Reject** the null hypothesis. This indicates that there is a linear relationship between X and Y.

Section 9.2

▶ Example 2 (pg. 460)   Finding a Regression Line

Enter the X-values into **L1** and the Y-values into **L2**. Press **STAT**, highlight **CALC** and select **4:LinReg(ax+b)**. This command has several options. One option allows you to store the regression equation into one of the Y-variables. To use this option, with the cursor flashing on the line **LinReg(ax+b)**, press **VARS**.

Highlight **Y-VARS**.

Select **1:Function** and press **ENTER**

Notice that **1:Y1** is highlighted. Press **ENTER**.

Press **ENTER**.

```
LinReg
 y=ax+b
 a=11.8244078
 b=35.30117105
 r²=.9404868083
 r=.9697869912
```

The output displays the general form of the regression equation: $y = ax+b$
followed by values for a and b. Next, r^2, the coefficient of determination, and r,
the correlation coefficient , are displayed. If you put the values of a and b into
the general equation, you obtain the specific linear equation for this data:
y= 11.82 + 35.30 x. Press **Y=** and see that this specific equation has been pasted
to **Y1**.

```
Plot1  Plot2  Plot3
\Y1₌11.824407800
243X+35.30117104
6452
\Y2=
\Y3=
\Y4=
\Y5=
```

Press **2ⁿᵈ STAT PLOT]** , select **1:Plot1**, turn **ON** Plot1, select **scatter plot**, set
Xlist to **L1** and **Ylist** to **L2**. Press **ZOOM** and **9**.

This picture displays a scatter plot of the data and the regression line. The picture indicates a strong positive linear correlation between X and Y, which is confirmed by the r-value of .970.

You can use the regression equation stored in **Y1** to predict Y-values for specific X-values. For example, suppose the duration of an eruption was equal to 1.95 minutes. Predict the time (in minutes) until the next eruption. In other words, for X = 1.95, what does the regression equation predict for Y? To find this value for Y, press **VARS**, highlight **Y-VARS**, select **1:Function**, press **ENTER**, select **1:Y1** and press **ENTER**. Press **(** 1.95 **)** and press **ENTER** .

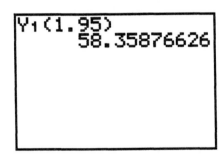

The output is a display of the predicted Y-value for X = 1.95.

▶ Exercise 15 (pg. 463)   Finding the Equation of the Regression
                           Line

Enter the X-values into **L1** and the Y-values into **L2**. Press **STAT**. Highlight
CALC, select **4:LinReg(ax+b)**, press **ENTER**. Press **VARS**, highlight **Y-
VARS**, select **1:Function**, press **ENTER** and select **1:Y1** and press **ENTER**.

Press **ENTER**.

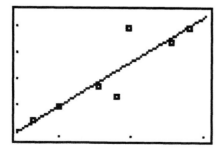

Using **a** and **b** from the output display, the resulting regression equation is y =
1.724 x + 79.73. Press **Y=** to confirm that the regression equation has been
stored in **Y1**. Press **ZOOM** and **9** for **ZoomStat** and a graph of the scatter plot
with the regression line will be displayed.

Next, you can use the regression equation to predict systolic blood pressure, Y,
for various ages, X. First, check the X-values that you will be using to confirm

that they are within (or close to) the range of the X-values in your data. The four X-values (18, 71, 29 and 55) meet this criteria.

Press **VARS**, highlight **Y-VARS**, select **1:Function** and press **ENTER**. Select **1:Y1** and press **ENTER**. Press (18) and **ENTER**.

```
Y₁(18)
       110.7580483




```

The predicted systolic blood pressure for the average 18-year-old male is 110.8.

Press **2ⁿᵈ** **[ENTRY]**, (found above the ENTER key). Move the cursor so that it is flashing on '1' in the number '18' and type in 71. Press **ENTER**.

```
Y₁(18)
       110.7580483
Y₁(71)
       202.1084004
■


```

The predicted systolic blood pressure for the average 71-year-old male is 202.1.

Press **2ⁿᵈ** **[ENTRY]** . Move the cursor so that it is flashing on '7' in the number '71' and type in 29. Press **ENTER**.

The predicted systolic blood pressure for the average 29-year-old male is 129.7.

Press **2ⁿᵈ** **[ENTRY]** . Move the cursor so that it is flashing on '2' in the number '29' and type in 55. Press **ENTER**. The predicted systolic blood pressure for the average 55-year-old male is 174.55.

◄

Section 9.3

▶ **Example 2 (pg. 471)** The Standard Error of the Estimate

Enter the data into **L1** and **L2**. Press **STAT**, highlight **CALC**, select **4:LinReg(ax+b)**, and press **ENTER**. Press **VARS**, highlight **Y-VARS**, select **1:Function**, press **ENTER**, select **1:Y1** and press **ENTER ENTER**.

The formula for s_e, the standard error of the estimate is $\sqrt{\dfrac{\sum (y_i - \hat{y}_i)^2}{n-2}}$. The values for $(y_i - \hat{y}_i)$, called Residuals, are automatically stored to a list called **RESID**. Press **2nd** **[LIST]** , select **7:RESID**. Press **STO**, **2nd** **[L3]** and **ENTER**. This stores the residuals to **L3**.

```
LRESID→L₃
{-.8097165992  -…
```

In the formula for s_e, the residuals, $(y_i - \hat{y}_i)$, are squared. To square these values and store them in **L4**, press **STAT**, select **1:Edit** and move the cursor to highlight the Listname **L4**. Press **ENTER**. Press **2nd** **[L3]** and the x^2 key.

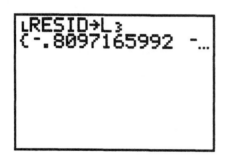

L2	L3	L4	4
225	-.8097	------	
184	-1.227		
220	14.482		
240	4.0445		
180	4.919		
184	-1.227		
186	-19.52		

L4 =L₃²

Press **ENTER**.

```
L2       L3       L4       4
225      -.8097   .65564
184      -1.227   1.5048
220      14.482   209.72
240      4.0445   16.358
180      4.919    24.197
184      -1.227   1.5048
186      -19.52   380.96
L4(1)=.6556409710...
```

Press **2ⁿᵈ** **[QUIT]** . Next, you need to find the sum of **L4**, $\sum (y_i - \hat{y}_i)^2$. Press **2ⁿᵈ** **[LIST]** . Highlight **MATH**, select **5:sum(** and press **2ⁿᵈ** **[L4]** . Close the parentheses and press **ENTER**.

```
sum(L4)
          635.3441296
```

Divide this sum by (number of observations – 2). In this example, (n - 2) = 6. Simply press ÷ 6 and press **ENTER**.

```
sum(L4)
          635.3441296
Ans/6
          105.8906883
```

Lastly, take the square root of this answer by pressing **2ⁿᵈ** **[√]** **2ⁿᵈ** **[ANS]** . Close the parentheses and press **ENTER**.

```
sum(L4)
          635.3441296
Ans/6
          105.8906883
√(Ans)
          10.29032012
■
```

The standard error of the estimate, s_e, is 10.29.

▶ Example 3 (pg. 473) Constructing a Prediction Interval

This example is a continuation of Example 2 on pg. 471. To construct a prediction interval for a specific X-value, x_o, you must calculate the maximum

error, E. The formula for E is: $E = t_c s_e \sqrt{(1 + \dfrac{1}{n} + \dfrac{n(x_o - \bar{x})^2}{n(\sum x^2) - (\sum x)^2}}$. The

critical value for t is found in the t-table. For this example, $t_c = 2.447$. The standard error, s_e, is 10.290.

To calculate $\bar{x}$, $\sum x^2$, and $(\sum x)^2$, press **VARS**, select **5:Statistics**. Highlight **2:** $\bar{x}$ and press **ENTER ENTER**. Notice that $\bar{x} = 1.975$. Press **VARS** again, select **5:Statistics**, highlight $\sum$, select **1:** $\sum x$ and press **ENTER ENTER**. So, $\sum x = 15.8$. Press **VARS** again, select **5:Statistics**, highlight $\sum$, select **2:** $\sum x^2$, and press **ENTER ENTER**. Notice that $\sum x^2 = 32.44$.

Next, calculate the maximum error, E, when $x_o = 2.1$ using the formula for E.

```
2.447*10.29*√(1+
1/8+8(2.1-1.975)
²/(8*32.44-15.8²
)
        26.85678531
```

The prediction interval is $\hat{y} \pm 26.857$. To find $\hat{y}$, the predicted value for y when x = 2.1, press **VARS**, highlight **Y-VARS**, select **1:Function** and press **ENTER**. Next select **1:Y1**, press **ENTER** and press **(2.1)**. Finally, press **ENTER**.

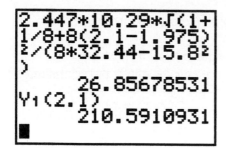

The prediction interval is 210.59 ± 26.857.

▶ Exercise 11 (pg. 475) Coefficient of Determination and
Standard Error of the Estimate

Enter the data into **L1** and **L2**. Press STAT, highlight **CALC**, select
4:LinReg(ax+b) and press ENTER. Next, press VARS, select **Y-VARS**, select
1:Function and press ENTER. Lastly, select **1:Y1** and press ENTER ENTER.

```
LinReg
 y=ax+b
 a=230.8314924
 b=-289.8094201
 r²=.9853951741
 r=.9926707279
 ■
```

The coefficient of determination, r^2, is .9854. This means that 98.54 % of the
variation of the Y-values is explained by the X-values.

To calculate s_e, press **2ⁿᵈ** **[LIST]** , select **1:RESID**, press ENTER, STO , **2ⁿᵈ**
[L3] ENTER. This stores the residuals to **L3**. In the formula for s_e, the
residuals, $(y_i - \hat{y}_i)$, are squared. To square these values and store them in **L4**,
press STAT, select **1:Edit** and move the cursor to highlight the Listname **L4**.
Press ENTER. Press **2ⁿᵈ** **[L3]** and the x^2 key. Press ENTER.

```
L2      L3      L4      4
123.2   43.679  1907.9
211.5   -29.6   876.34
385.5   -17.19  295.33
475.1   -19.92  396.71
641.1   30.667  940.44
716.9   -55.12  3037.7
768.2   -26.9   723.53
L4(1)=1907.857859...
```

Press **2ⁿᵈ** **[QUIT]** . Next, you need to find the sum of **L4**, $\sum (y_i - \hat{y}_i)^2$. Press
2ⁿᵈ **[LIST]** . Highlight **MATH**, select **5:sum(** and press **2ⁿᵈ** **[L4]** . Close the
parentheses and press ENTER.

```
 r²=.9853951741
 r=.9926707279

∟RESID→L₃
{43.67903226  -2…
sum(L₄)
       11439.53051
■
```

Divide this sum by (number of observations – 2). In this example, (n - 2) = 9.
Simply press ÷ 9 and press **ENTER**.

```
∟RESID→L₃
{43.67903226  -2…
sum(L₄)
       11439.53051
Ans/9
       1271.058945
■
```

Lastly, take the square root of this answer by pressing **2ⁿᵈ** [√] **2ⁿᵈ** [ANS] .
Close the parentheses and press **ENTER**.

```
{43.67903226  -2…
sum(L₄)
       11439.53051
Ans/9
       1271.058945
√(Ans)
       35.65191363
■
```

◀

▶ Technology Lab (pg. 483)   Tar, Nicotine and Carbon Monoxide

Exercises 1-2: Enter the data into **L1**, **L2**, **L3** and **L4**. To construct the scatter plots, press **2ⁿᵈ** **[STAT PLOT]**, select **1:Plot1** and press **ENTER**. Turn **ON** Plot1. Select **scatter plot** for **Type**. Enter the appropriate labels for **Xlist** and **Ylist** to construct each of the scatter plots.

Exercises 3: To find the correlation coefficients, press **STAT**, highlight **CALC** and select **4:LinReg(ax+b)** and enter the labels of the columns you are using for the correlation. For example, to find the correlation coefficient for "weight" and "carbon monoxide", press **2ⁿᵈ** **[L3]** **[,]** **2ⁿᵈ** **[L4]**.

Press **ENTER** and notice that the correlation coefficient for weight and carbon monoxide is .3616.

Exercise 4: To find the regression equations, press **STAT**, highlight **CALC** and select **4:LinReg(ax+b)** and enter the labels of the columns you are using for the regression. For example, to find the regression equation for "tar" and "carbon monoxide", press **2ⁿᵈ** **[L1]** **[,]** **2ⁿᵈ** **[L4]** .

Exercise 5: Use the regression equations found in Exercise 4 to do the predictions.

◀

Chi-Square Tests and the F-Distribution

Section 10.2

▶ **Example 3 (pg. 509)** Chi-Square Independence Test

Test the hypotheses: H_o :The number of days spent exercising per week is *independent* of gender vs. H_a : The number of days spent exercising per week *depends* on gender. The first step is to enter the data in the table into **Matrix A**. On the TI-83, press **MATRX**, highlight **EDIT** and press **ENTER**. On the TI-83 Plus, press 2nd [**MATRX**] . (MATRX is found above the x^{-1} key.) Highlight **EDIT** and press **ENTER**.

On the top row of the display, enter the size of the matrix. The matrix has 2 rows and 4 columns, so press **2** , press the right arrow key, and press **4**. Press **ENTER**. Enter the first value, 40, and press **ENTER**. Enter the second value, 53, and press **ENTER**. Continue this process and fill the matrix.

Press 2nd [Quit] . To perform the test of independence, press **STAT**, highlight **TESTS**, and select **C: χ^2-Test** and press **ENTER**.

For **Observed**, [A] should be selected. If [A] is not already selected, press
MATRX, highlight **NAMES**, select 1:[A] and press ENTER. For, **Expected**, [B]
should be selected. Move the cursor to the next line and select **Calculate** and
press ENTER.

The output displays the test statistic and the P-value. Since the P-value is greater
than α, the correct decision is to **Fail to Reject** the null hypothesis. This means
that the number of days per week spent exercising is *independent* of gender.

Or, you could highlight **Draw** and press ENTER.

This output displays the χ^2 –**curve** with the area associated with the P-value
shaded in. The test statistic and the P-value are also displayed.

▶ Exercise 5 (pg. 511)   Chi-Square Test for Independence

Test the hypotheses: H_o :The Result (improvement or no change) is *independent* of Treatment (drug or placebo) vs. H_a : The Result *depends* on the Treatment. Enter the data in the table into **Matrix A**. Press MATRX, highlight **EDIT** and press ENTER.

On the top row of the display, enter the size of the matrix. The matrix has 2 rows and 2 columns, so press ▓ , press the right arrow key, and press ▓. Press ENTER. Enter the first value, 39, and press ENTER. Enter the second value, 25, and press ENTER. Continue this process and fill the matrix.

```
MATRIX[A]  2 ×2
[ 39     25        ]
[ 54     70        ]



2,2=70
```

Press 2nd [Quit] . Press STAT, highlight **TESTS**, and select **C: χ^2-Test** and press ENTER. For **Observed**, **[A]** should be selected. If **[A]** is not already selected, press MATRX, highlight **NAMES**, select **1:[A]** and press ENTER. For, **Expected**, **[B]** should be selected. Move the cursor to the next line and select **Calculate** and press ENTER.

```
χ²-Test
 χ²=5.106317432
 P=.0238388683
 df=1


```

The output displays the test statistic and the P-value. Since the P-value is less than α , the correct decision is to **Reject** the null hypothesis. The correct recommendation is to use the drug as part of the treatment.

◀

Section 10.3

▶ Example 3 (pg. 519) Performing a Two-Sample F-Test

Test the hypotheses: $H_o : \sigma_1^2 \leq \sigma_2^2$ vs. $H_a : \sigma_1^2 > \sigma_2^2$. The sample statistics are: $s_1^2 = 144$, $n_1 = 10$, $s_2^2 = 100$ and $n_2 = 21$. Press STAT, highlight **TESTS** and select **D:2-SampFTest**. For **Inpt**, select **Stats** and press ENTER. On the next line, enter s_1, the standard deviation under the old system. The standard deviation is the square root of the variance, so press 2nd [$\sqrt{\ }$] and enter 144. Enter n_1 on the next line. Next, enter the standard deviation under the new system by pressing 2nd [$\sqrt{\ }$] 100. Enter n_2 on the next line. Highlight $> \sigma_2$ for the alternative hypothesis and press ENTER. Select **Calculate** and press ENTER.

```
2-SampFTest
 σ1>σ2
 F=1.44
 P=.2369000822
 Sx1=12
 Sx2=10
↓n1=10
```

The output displays the alternative hypothesis, the test statistic, the P-value and the sample statistics. Since the P-value is greater than α, the correct decision is to **Fail to Reject** the null hypothesis. There is not enough evidence to conclude that the new system decreased the variance in waiting times.

You could also select **Draw** and press ENTER.

The output displays the F-distribution with the area associated with the P-value shaded in.

▶ Exercise 19 (pg. 522)   Comparing Two Variances

Test the hypotheses: $H_o : \sigma_1^2 \leq \sigma_2^2$ vs. $H_a : \sigma_1^2 > \sigma_2^2$. The sample statistics
are: $s_1 = 0.7$, $n_1 = 25$, $s_2 = 0.5$ and $n_2 = 21$. Press **STAT**, highlight **TESTS**
and select **D:2-SampFTest**. For **Inpt**, select **Stats** and press **ENTER**. On the
next line, enter s_1, the standard deviation under the old procedure. Enter n_1 on
the next line. Next, enter the standard deviation and sample size for the new
procedure and press **ENTER**. Highlight $> \sigma_2$ for the alternative hypothesis and
press **ENTER**. Select **Calculate** and press **ENTER**.

```
2-SampFTest
 σ1>σ2
 F=1.96
 P=.0653066513
 Sx1=.7
 Sx2=.5
↓n1=25
```

The output displays the alternative hypothesis, the test statistic, the P-value and
the sample statistics. Since the P-value is less than α, the correct decision is to
Reject the null hypothesis. The data supports the hospital's claim that the
standard deviation of the waiting times has decreased.

◀

Section 10.4

▶ Example 2 (pg. 529) Performing an ANOVA Test

Test the hypotheses: $H_o : \mu_1 = \mu_2 = \mu_3$ vs. H_a :at least one mean is different from the others. Enter the data into **L1, L2, and L3**. Press **STAT**, highlight **TESTS** and select **F:ANOVA(** and press **ENTER**, 2nd [L1] , 2nd [L2] , 2nd [L3].

Press **ENTER** and the results will be displayed on the screen.

```
One-way ANOVA
 F=6.13023478
 P=.0063828069
 Factor
  df=2
  SS=1806.46667
↓ MS=903.233333
■
```

```
One-way ANOVA
↑ MS=903.233333
 Error
  df=27
  SS=3978.2
  MS=147.340741
 Sxp=12.1383994
■
```

The output displays the test statistic, F = 6.13, and the P-value, p = .00638. Since the P-value is less than α, the correct decision is to **Reject** the null hypothesis.

This indicates that there is a difference in the mean flight times of the three airlines.

The output also displays all the information that is needed to set up an ANOVA table like the table on pg. 526 of your textbook.

Variation	Sum of Squares	Degrees of Freedom	Mean Squares	F
Between	1806.5	2	903.2	903.2 / 147.3
Within	3978.2	27	147.3	

Note: The TI-83 labels variation "Between" samples as variation due to the "Factor". Also, variation "Within" samples is labeled as "Error".

The final item in the output is the pooled standard deviation, Sxp = 12.14.

▶ Exercise 1 (pg. 531)   Performing an ANOVA Test

Test the hypotheses: $H_o : \mu_1 = \mu_2 = \mu_3$ vs. H_a :at least one mean is different from the others. Enter the data into **L1, L2,** and **L3**. Press STAT, highlight **TESTS** and select **F:ANOVA(** and press ENTER, 2nd [L1] , 2nd [L2] , 2nd [L3]. Press ENTER and the results will be displayed on the screen.

```
One-way ANOVA
 F=1.259699793
 p=.2998881447
 Factor
   df=2
   SS=1.63002551
↓ MS=.815012756
```

```
One-way ANOVA
↑ MS=.815012756
 Error
   df=27
   SS=17.4687212
   MS=.646989672
 Sxp=.804356682
```

The output displays the test statistic, F = 1.26, and the P-value, p = 0.299888. Since the P-value is greater than α, the correct decision is to **Fail to Reject** the null hypothesis. The data does not support the claim that at least one mean cost per month is different.

◀

> ▶ Exercise 10 (pg. 534) Performing an ANOVA Test

Test the hypotheses: $H_o : \mu_1 = \mu_2 = \mu_3 = \mu_4$ vs. H_a :at least one mean is different from the others. Enter the data into **L1, L2, L3** and **L4** . Press STAT, highlight **TESTS** and select **F:ANOVA(** and press ENTER, 2nd [L1] , 2nd [L2] , 2nd [L3] , 2nd [L4]. Press ENTER and the results will be displayed on the screen.

```
One-way ANOVA
 F=8.4596944
 p=2.1962975E-4
 Factor
   df=3
   SS=61130.6776
↓ MS=20376.8925
```

```
One-way ANOVA
↑ MS=20376.8925
 Error
   df=36
   SS=86713.3134
   MS=2408.70315
 Sxp=49.0785406
```

The output displays the test statistic, F = 8.46, and the P-value, p = .0002196. Since the P-value is less than α, the correct decision is to **Reject** the null hypothesis. The data supports the claim that the mean energy consumption for at least one region is different.

◀

▶ Technology Lab (pg. 536)   Crash Tests

Exercise 2: One method of testing to see if a set of data is approximately normal is to use a Normal Probability Plot. To test the data in **L1**, press 2nd **[STAT PLOT]** , select Plot 1 and turn **ON** Plot1. For **Type**, select the last icon on the second line. For **Data List**, press 2nd **[L1]**. For **Data Axis**, select **X**. For **Mark**, select the first icon. Press ZOOM and 9 to display the normal plot.

Data that is normally distributed will plot as a straight line. Although this graph is not perfectly straight, it is fairly linear and it is therefore reasonable to conclude that the data is approximately normal. Repeat this process to check the other datasets for normality.

Exercise 3: Test the hypotheses: $H_o \ \sigma_1^{\ 2} = \sigma_2^{\ 2}$ vs. $H_a : \sigma_1^{\ 2} \neq \sigma_2^2$ for each pair of samples. This test requires values for s_1 and s_2. To obtain these values, enter the data into **L1, L2** and **L3**. To find the standard deviation for **L1**, press STAT, highlight **CALC** and press L1 ENTER. To find the standard deviation for **L2**, press STAT, highlight **CALC**, press **[L2]** ENTER. Repeat this process to get the standard deviation of **L3**.

For each comparison, press STAT, highlight **TESTS** and select **D:2-SampFTest**. For **Inpt**, select **Stats** and press ENTER. On the next line, enter s_1, the larger of the two standard deviations. Enter n_1, the corresponding sample size, on the next line. Next, enter the smaller of the two standard deviations and then, the sample size. Highlight $\neq \sigma_2^{\ 2}$ for the alternative hypothesis and press ENTER. Select **Calculate** and press ENTER.

Exercise 4: Test the hypotheses: $H_o : \mu_1 = \mu_2 = \mu_3$ vs. H_a :at least one mean is different from the others. Press STAT, highlight **TESTS** and select **F:ANOVA(** and press ENTER, 2nd **[L1]** , 2nd **[L2]** , 2nd **[L3]** . Press ENTER and the results will be displayed on the screen.

Exercise 5: Repeat Exercises 1 - 4 using this second set of data.